WORLDS
WORST©
GLADIATOR

First published in Great Britain by Scribo MMXIX
Scribo, an imprint of
The Salariya Book Company
25 Marlborough Place, Brighton, BN1 1UB

ISBN 978-1-912537-26-6

Book design by David Salariya

Printed and bound in China

The text for this book is set in Century Schoolbook
The display type is Jacob Riley

www.salariya.com

Illustrations: Isobel Lundie

THE LONG-LOST SECRET DIARY OF THE WORLD'S WORST GLADIATOR

Written by
Tim Collins

Illustrated by
Isobel Lundie

SCRIBO
a SALARIYA imprint

Chapter I

⊢—⊣

Life in Pompeii, 79 AD

April 11

Septimus and Marina made me play gladiators with them in the forum today. I kept suggesting that we play dice or something sensible, but they insisted we whack each other with sticks and pretend to be battling in an arena.

They tell me you need skill and strategy to win these contests. No you don't. You just need to hit the other person really hard.

They know much more about gladiators than me because I never go to the amphitheatre. I don't find the sight of all that blood gushing into the sand exciting, I just find it disgusting. I have no idea how everyone can sit there and munch their snacks while it's happening.

According to Septimus and Marina, I should make the best gladiator because I look most like one. I'm twice as tall and broad as them, and I could pass for much older than my age.

But I don't want to be a gladiator, because getting injured in front of a massive crowd isn't my idea of fun. Apparently that makes me weird.

Septimus was a secutor as usual. He was born with a red mark in the shape of a dagger on his thigh, and he's convinced that means he'll be a

secutor when he's older. Marina chose to be a Thracian, and I had to be a retiarius. I gave up after a few hits, rolled onto the floor and stuck my finger in the air for mercy.

Septimus looked up to the imaginary crowd, announced that they wanted me to be killed, and mimed stabbing me in the heart. I pretended to die, which at least meant the game was over.

GET REAL

In Ancient Rome, gladiators battled in huge arenas for the entertainment of bloodthirsty crowds. There were several different types, each with their own weapons. A secutor had a dagger and a rectangular shield, a retiarius had a net and a trident and a Thracian had a small shield and a short, curved sword.

April III

We didn't have to play gladiators today, but that didn't stop Septimus and Marina going on and on about them.

We went down to the amphitheatre, even though there were no games on. Septimus strode out into the arena and acted out all the battles he'd seen. Like he'd last five minutes in a real one.

I sat there and listened to the whole thing, mostly because there's nothing else to do here in Pompeii.

The only interesting thing that's ever happened here is when the ground trembled so much that one of the temples fell down. But that was before I was born, so I only know about it from my parents.

I keep telling Dad he should let me move to Rome and live with his brother Quintus. Exciting stuff happens there all the time.

But he always refuses because it's too dangerous. I don't care. I'd rather be in danger in Rome than bored here.

GET REAL

A large earthquake hit the town of Pompeii in 62 AD, damaging many of the buildings. A much more famous disaster was to happen 17 years later, when Mount Vesuvius erupted and destroyed the town.

April IV

I don't know what I've done to please the gods, but they've granted my wish. I'm actually going to Rome!

Dad makes fish sauce for a living, and it's called 'Neptune's Choice Luxury Garum'. Soon he's going to stay with Quintus so he can sell some to the people of Rome.

After loads of pleading, he's agreed to let me go.

Because Rome is so dangerous, I've agreed to remain in Quintus's house all day while they go out and sell the garum. I'm not going to, of course. I'm going out to see the big city for myself.

Hmm. I'm not sure I should be admitting that in this scroll, though. What if Dad reads it and changes his mind?

I'll just have to keep this scroll tucked into the belt of my tunic at all times from now on. That way I can write the absolute truth without anyone reading it.

GET REAL

Garum was a type of fish sauce that was popular in Ancient Rome. It was made by chopping fish such as sardines into tiny pieces, adding eggs and entrails, and leaving the whole stinky mess in the sun for six weeks to ferment. You can follow this recipe if you like, but it sounds pretty disgusting, and your parents might assume the cat has been sick and throw it away before you get a chance to taste it.

April V

Septimus and Marina were really jealous of my Rome trip. They kept listing all the famous gladiators I could go and watch.

They were shocked when I told them I wasn't going to bother seeing a single one. There will be so many new things to see there. Why should I go to the amphitheatre when we've got one here?

April VI

We set off while it was still dark. The furthest I've ever been from home before is Herculaneum, which is only three hours away, and I think long journeys are going to take a lot of getting used to.

I enjoy riding around town on Dad's cart, as it's quite fun when it bumps up and down. Let's just say the fun wears off after a while. Then the pain kicks in. Right now I feel like I've been dragged along behind a cart instead of riding in one.

I tried to distract myself by asking about Rome,

but Dad kept going on about how dishonest everyone there is. He made me promise again to stay in Quin's house, and I did, which I feel quite guilty about.

But come on. I'm not going to make do with looking at Rome through my uncle's window

I can't wait to finally see Rome...

when I could be out there enjoying it for myself.
I'm sure Dad will understand if I get found out.

Dad wouldn't even pay for an inn after our
uncomfortable day. Instead we're taking turns
to sleep at the side of the road while the other
keeps watch over the cart, the oxen and the
precious garum.

Dad never spends money if he can avoid it. He wouldn't replace my last tunic until it was full of holes and he wouldn't replace our last slave Calpurnia until she could barely lift up the serving dishes.

GET REAL

The Ancient Romans built a network of long, straight roads spanning from England to North Africa. Many of them were still used after the fall of the Roman Empire, and some great examples can still be seen in places such as Pompeii.

These days it wouldn't take long to travel the 241 kilometres from Pompeii to Rome, but back in the first century AD, it was an epic trek.

April XIV

We have finally made it to Rome. We arrived
last night, and Quintus laid on a wonderful
feast to celebrate our arrival. His slaves brought
us dishes loaded with mushrooms, dates, eggs,
sardines, goat, hare and flamingo with dates.

GET REAL

*Most ordinary Romans didn't have stoves
for cooking, so they bought snacks such as
stew and porridge from street stalls. But rich
people could throw lavish dinner parties with
several courses. Instead of sitting on chairs,
they would lie on couches as they ate.*

*If you fancy trying flamingo with dates, here's
how to make it. First wash your flamingo
and place it in a pan with water and vinegar.
Bring to the boil and thicken the sauce with
flour. Then add dates and spices. Serve it to
your whole family to make sure they never
ask you to make dinner again.*

It was amazing, but the couch I was lying on was so comfortable after all those days on the road that I fell asleep after just six courses.

When I woke this morning, Dad and Quintus were just heading out to sell the garum.

Quintus has left a slave called Libius to look after me. Luckily, Libius is too busy to do a good job. As well as minding me, he's got to buy and prepare tonight's food, clean the whole house and wash loads of clothes.

I told him I'd mind myself so he could get on with all his other jobs, and he agreed. Which means I'll be free to sneak away as soon as he goes out to the shops.

LATER ON

As soon as Libius left, I dashed outside.

Everyone on the street seemed to be in a massive hurry and I found myself swept along with them.

Everywhere looked the same at first. Tall houses loomed over narrow streets packed with busy, noisy people, and covered in horse and ox poo. Every so often the buildings would open onto a market or a square.

I was worried that I might get lost, but the street soon sloped down, and I could tell where I was.

Below me was the forum, with its temples, courthouses and statues. Beyond it was another hill, lined with grand houses and palaces.

As long as I could remember which hill I'd come from, I was safe to wander around down there.

Rome is just as exciting and exhausting as I was expecting. I saw men giving speeches from a high platform, important-looking men in thick woollen togas, rich women with their faces powdered with chalk and even some angry men arguing over a game of dice. These ones looked like they were about to kill each other, so I rushed away from them.

Most people seemed very friendly, though. A few of them smiled and waved, and some even shouted, 'Cassius' and looked shocked to see me. I've no idea what that was all about.

Before long, I climbed back up the hill to Uncle Quintus's house. I thought Libius might be worried about me, but he was concentrating so hard on scrubbing the floor he hadn't even noticed I was gone. I wonder if I could get away with staying out longer tomorrow.

GET REAL

Rome is said to be built on seven hills, which began as separate settlements. It's estimated that there were a million people in Rome by the first century AD. These days there are 2,800,000 people living in the city.

April XV

Dad and Quintus went out this morning, leaving Libius in charge of me again. He was soon busy preparing vegetables, leaving me free to wander back down to the forum.

More people shouted 'Cassius' at me as I walked around. I wondered what it meant. I hoped it was a bit of local slang for someone cool.

At one point a man with red hair clasped my shoulder and yelled, 'I bet Lucius wouldn't be happy if he saw you here.'

I guessed this was one of the rude locals Dad had warned me about. I struggled free of his grasp and backed away.

He turned to a plump woman who was looking at some sandals on a market stall and shouted, 'Hey Calpurnia! Here's that Cassius bloke we saw fighting last week.'

Fighting? I hoped they hadn't mistaken me for one of those angry men I'd seen playing dice. That was exactly the sort of trouble I wanted to avoid.

The woman looked up from the stall.

'Oh yeah,' she said. She wandered over and prodded me in the chest. 'Shouldn't you be in

the gladiator school?'

A girl wearing a red shawl came charging over.

'Did someone say Cassius was here?' she asked. She spotted me and clasped her hands to her cheeks. 'Oh my gods,' she said. 'You're my favourite fighter. That battle you had with Paulus last week was amazing. Did you escape or something? That's so exciting.'

A bald man who was munching a piece of bread tapped me on the shoulder. 'Quick question,' he said, with his mouth full. 'What's Claudia like in real life?'

A crowd was forming around me. Some of them were wandering over from a nearby slave auction. I wondered how I could possibly be more interesting than that.

I stepped back. 'You've got it wrong,' I said. 'I'm not a gladiator. I don't even like gladiators.'

'Do you think we'll get a reward for returning him to Lucius?' asked the man with red hair.

'Don't try and touch him,' said his wife. 'He might not have his trident with him, but you still wouldn't stand a chance.'

I kept backing away, but the crowd pushed forward. There was no point in trying to reason with them, so I turned and fled.

'Told you he was on the run,' I heard the man with red hair saying. 'We'd have got good money for taking him back.'

It was pretty frightening while it was going on.

But now I'm back in Uncle Quintus's house, I can see the funny side. I obviously look a lot like a gladiator called Cassius, and they all thought I'd escaped from my lanista.

I might even go over to the gladiator school tomorrow and see this Cassius for myself. I bet he looks nothing like me, though.

GET REAL

Gladiators had an unusual position in Roman society. The successful ones were like sports stars, with thousands of fans. But they were still slaves, belonging to their trainer, or lanista.

Chapter 2
—
Tricked!

April XVI

Now that it's over, I think I can say it for certain: that was the worst day of my life. At least I still have my scroll so I can write about it. That's something.

Libius was once again in charge of me this morning, so I sneaked out and made my way over to the gladiator school, which was at the back of a huge amphitheatre.

Nobody stopped me as I strolled in. The school was a square courtyard surrounded by small, dark rooms. In the middle was a circular arena with a few tiers of wooden seats rising up.

There was a retiarius practising in the arena with a net and wooden trident, and I could tell straight away that it was Cassius.

Marcus

Rounder head

Toga

Trident

Loincloth

Cassius

Sometimes people tell me I look like someone, but I can't see it. I could this time.

If Cassius hadn't been dressed so differently, I could have been looking into a mirror. He was wearing a loincloth with a belt and a thick bronze arm guard, but in every other way he looked just like me. He even had the same short brown hair.

34

He smiled as I approached.

'They never told me I had a long-lost brother,' he said, slapping me on the back. The force almost made me fall over.

'I went to the forum yesterday and everyone told me I looked like a gladiator called Cassius,' I said. 'So I thought I'd come here and look for myself.'

Cassius glanced around, his smile slipping.

'Seriously?' he asked. 'That's the first time anyone's ever said that to you? I'd expect you to get it all the time.'

'This is just my third day in Rome,' I said. 'I'm actually here on holiday.'

'So you're not a slave, then?' he asked.

'Of course not,' I said. 'My father owns a successful fish-sauce business.'

I remembered that he was just a slave despite all his fame, and it wasn't a good idea to upset him. Even if his trident was only made of wood, he could probably do a lot of damage with it.

'Not that there would be anything wrong with being a slave,' I said. 'Some of them are good workers. Not the one who's meant to be looking after me right now, mind. He's awful. But a lot of them are great value for money.'

Cassius scratched his chin, then pointed at my tunic.

'Hey, I've just had a really funny idea!' he said. 'Why don't we swap clothes and pretend to be each other for a while? I'll call the other gladiators over and we'll see if we can fool them.'

36

I found myself grinning at the idea of this. I hadn't played a practical joke on anyone for ages, though Septimus and Marina had played a lot on me.

'Sure,' I said. 'Why not?'

I removed my tunic, while Cassius handed over his armour, trident and loincloth. My scroll and stylus fell onto the floor when I took my belt off, so I tucked them into my loincloth to make sure I didn't lose them. That was the one sensible thing I did all day.

I pulled Cassius's arm guard on. It didn't seem like it would give much protection against swords, daggers and spears. But I supposed it wouldn't be as exciting for the crowds if the fighters were too safe.

When we were wearing each other's clothes,

Cassius creased up with laughter. I didn't find it quite as funny as he did, but I did my best to chuckle along.

'Right,' I said. 'Should we go and play our trick now?'

'Sure,' he said. 'I'll just go and fetch the others.'

He darted out of the arena. I wandered over to a gap between the seats and saw him sprinting out of the main exit. Why would the other gladiators be outside the school?

'Oi Cassius!' cried a voice from behind me. 'I didn't say you could take a break.'

A man was pacing towards me. He was huge but in pretty bad shape. He was bald except for a few straggly black hairs on the back and sides

of his head. He was wearing a dirty white tunic and a ragged pair of sandals. I guessed this was Lucius, the lanista they'd mentioned in the forum.

'Get back to your training, Cassius!' he shouted. His flabby cheeks were flushing red and I could hear him snorting.

I looked over my shoulder to see where Cassius was. Then the horrible truth hit me. I was wearing Cassius's outfit. I looked just like him. As far as Lucius was concerned, I was him.

'Wait,' I said. 'I'm not Cassius. This is all just a joke that's gone wrong. The real Cassius just ran away. You could catch him if you go now.'

Lucius grabbed my arm and looked into my eyes. I tried to pull away to escape his sour breath,

but he held me firm. He was surprisingly strong for someone who looked so unfit.

'This is because of that blow you took yesterday, isn't it?' he asked. 'I thought it looked nasty.'

'No,' I said. 'I'm not Cassius. Honest.'

Lucius spoke to me in a slow, patient voice, as if he were addressing a young child. 'You are Cassius,' he said. 'You took a heavy blow to the head in your last fight, which made you lose your memory. It happens sometimes. But if you keep training, it might come back. I paid a lot of money for you, and you have some good fights coming up.'

I didn't like the sound of this, especially the bit about fights. I struggled free of Lucius's grasp and ran towards the gap between the seats.

I heard his sandals thudding on the ground behind me, and his hand slammed down on my shoulder.

'Please let me go!' I shouted. 'I'm not Cassius.'

'I think you need some time alone to think about it,' said Lucius.

He twisted my arm behind my back and marched me over to a small room at the back of the courtyard.

'My Dad's rich!' I shouted. 'He'll give you as much garum as you want if you let me go.'

'I don't want revolting fish sauce!' he said. 'I want my retiarius to stop acting weird so he can get back to training.'

He shoved me into a tiny, dark cell with a bucket in one corner and a pile of straw in the other. Then he closed the door and locked it behind me.

I'm still inside now. I keep trying to convince myself that Dad will work out where I am and come to rescue me, but I don't think he will.

I didn't tell anyone I was coming here. And I don't even like gladiators, so it's the last place Dad would look. And he can't check everywhere in a city this size.

I'm starting to wonder if I'll be trapped here forever.

GET REAL

Gladiators lived in places known as 'schools'. They would sleep, eat and undergo a tough training regime in them. Each gladiator would practise with wooden versions of the weapons they used in their battles.

April XVII

I got that last bit wrong. I won't be stuck here forever. This is because I'm going to die the day after tomorrow.

That's the day of my first battle in the amphitheatre. Except Lucius doesn't think it's my first, because he thinks I'm Cassius and that I've already won loads. He has no idea he's sending me out to certain death.

I stayed up most of the night, shouting and rattling my door.

'He's still confused because of that knock on his head,' I heard Lucius explaining to the person in the next room. 'He'll snap out of it soon.'

Eventually I fell down to my straw in exhaustion. I can't have slept for long when Lucius opened the door, letting bright sunlight in.

I leapt to my feet and dashed outside.

'Thank gods you're releasing me,' I said. 'What made you realise your mistake?'

'Don't start all that again,' said Lucius. He pointed over to the small wooden arena. 'I want you to get some training in before breakfast. You've got a big fight in two days' time.'

'I'm not Cassius,' I said.

Lucius just glared at me and pointed at the arena. I got the feeling that if I said anything else, I wouldn't have to wait until the day after tomorrow to be killed.

I skulked over to the arena.

'Haven't you forgotten something?' asked Lucius.

I turned and saw he was holding the net and wooden trident Cassius had given me yesterday.

'You and Decimus are on last,' he said, handing them over. 'Make it good.'

I wandered through the gap in the seats into the arena. Standing on the far side was one

of the strongest men I'd ever seen. He was a
secutor, with a helmet that covered his face, a
curved shield and a wooden dagger. His muscly
arms and legs were marked with deep scars,
and thick blue veins were standing out on his
arms and chest.

'Did you hear that we're on last again?'
asked Decimus. 'It's always us, isn't it?'

'Don't tell me you think I'm Cassius too?' I
asked. 'I can't look that much like him, can I?'

Decimus nodded, shaking his heavy helmet up
and down.

'Right,' he said. 'Lucius warned me you've
had a funny turn since I got you on the head
with my shield the other day. Sorry about that.
It's all part of the game, though, isn't it?'

I tried to think of a way to explain myself I hadn't already tried. It was no use. Nobody was going to believe me. At least everyone would realise I wasn't Cassius when I tried to fight.

I screamed, held out my wooden trident and charged towards Decimus. He blocked me with his shield and whipped his dagger round until the blunt tip was against my heart.

'You'd be dead,' he said. 'And what's worse, the crowd wouldn't even have been entertained.'

I stepped back to the far side of the arena and ran at him again.

This time I didn't even get near him. I tripped over my net and fell flat on my face. He swooped down and held his dagger against my neck.

'You'd be dead again,' he said. 'Though at

least this time the crowd would have had a laugh first.'

I got up and tried again. This time Decimus ducked aside and I couldn't make myself stop. I slammed my wooden trident right into one of the front row seats.

'This time you wouldn't be dead,' said Decimus. 'But someone in the crowd would be. That wouldn't go down too well.'

I tried again and again and failed every time.

Decimus took off his helmet and stared at me with his small, dark eyes.

'You've really forgotten how to fight, haven't you?' he asked.

'Yes,' I said. 'No. I never knew how in the

first place. I'm not Cassius.'

'I'm going to have to fight you properly when we're in front of the crowd,' he said. 'You know that, don't you? And unless you get your memory back, I'm going to kill you.'

My hands trembled, shaking the net and trident.

'No hard feelings, though,' he said. 'It's all part of the game.'

GET REAL

It's often thought that gladiators always battled to the death, but most of the time both fighters would survive. Gladiators were very valuable. Their owners spent time and money training them, so they'd want them to last longer than a single fight.

April XVIII

Lucius came in with a bowl of porridge this morning.

I slurped some down, but it had a horrible bitter taste that made me gag. I peered into the bowl and saw some black specks of dust had fallen into it.

'I think there's something in my porridge,' I said, holding the bowl up.

'Of course there is,' said Lucius. 'It's ash, to build your strength up. You always have that before a big fight, remember?'

I shrugged, and forced the disgusting mixture down.

'It sounds like you've forgotten a lot,' said Lucius. 'Decimus tells me you couldn't remember how to fight yesterday.'

'Yes,' I said. 'Except that I never knew how to fight in the first place. I haven't lost my memory at all, as I've explained.'

I made myself swallow more of the foul porridge.

'He says you'll be killed if the fight goes ahead tomorrow,' said Lucius. 'Is that true?'

'Yes,' I said.

Lucius nodded. 'Very well, then,' he said.

'What?' I asked. 'You mean I don't have to fight?'

'No,' said Lucius. 'The fight can still go ahead. I mean you'll just have to die.

Everyone's always complaining that I don't often let a fighter die. It will shut them all up when they see you coughing the last of your blood into the sand tomorrow.'

I let my spoon drop onto the plate. All this talk of death had made me lose my appetite.

'It's a shame, though,' said Lucius. 'I paid a lot of money for you. I was hoping you had a lot more fights left in you.'

He wandered away with his back bent and his shoulders slumped. He seemed almost as sad as Mum was when her clay figure of the goddess Juno broke. I supposed it was the same sort of thing, finding out that your best possession is no longer any use.

So now I have to wait in this room until tomorrow afternoon. After the beast shows and

the battle recreations, Lucius will take me to the amphitheatre and I'll be killed.

It looks like my scroll will end here, then. Goodbye, everyone. I take back everything I said about Pompeii being small and boring. I wish I'd stayed there now.

GET REAL

As well as gladiators, entertainment in a Roman amphitheatre would include musicians, jugglers, recreations of famous battles and beast shows. In these, prisoners would be torn to pieces by hungry lions, tigers and bears.

Chapter 3

A Dangerous Life

April XIX

So guess what? I'm still here.

I'm so relieved to still be alive that this cramped, smelly cell feels like luxury.

I thought I'd be lying dead in a puddle of my own blood on the floor of the arena right now. And that I'd whizz off to the afterlife to be punished by the Furies for my cowardice.

But none of that happened because I won. Sort of.

Soon after lunch I could hear the crowd cheering the beast shows and I felt my stomach flip. The show had started, and it would end in my death.

Sextus

Paulus

Claudia

Rufus

Eventually Lucius came to collect me. As well as Decimus, there were four other gladiators with him – a Thracian with red hair called Rufus, a hoplomachus with a wide bronze helmet called Paulus, a Samnite with a curved red shield called Sextus and a gladiatrix with blonde hair called Claudia.

60

They were all very different, but some were just as tall and broad as me. I almost felt like I fitted in, except that they were all capable of surviving an arena fight and I wasn't, or so I thought.

Lucius led us through a dark underground tunnel and up a flight of steps into a corridor that led straight out onto the arena floor.

I hung back with Decimus, Rufus and Paulus, while Sextus and Claudia strode out to fight.

I looked around the corner at the endless tiers of spectators rising high into the sky. Tens of thousands of people were there to watch me die.

Waves of cheers and boos echoed all around me, and I felt dizzy.

I tugged on Decimus's arm guard.

'Would it be okay if you didn't kill me?' I asked. 'I'm not really a gladiator, so it's not fair on me.'

'But it wouldn't be fair on the crowd if I didn't,' said Decimus. 'They expect me to do my best. It's all about entertaining the fans at the end of the day. They just want to come here, relax, forget their troubles.'

I didn't particularly care about their troubles. Whatever problems they had, at least they weren't about to be murdered for looking like someone else.

'Listen,' I said. 'You could just pretend to kill me, couldn't you? Then when they throw me onto the pile of bodies, I can sneak away without anyone noticing.'

'It wouldn't work,' said Decimus. 'Charon

will make totally sure you're dead before dragging you off.'

He pointed to a man in a black cape standing at the side of the arena. He was meant to be Charon, the ferryman of the underworld. There was a huge metal hammer in his hand, and it looked like it was covered in splodges of blood.

GET REAL

The Romans believed that when you died, a ferryman called Charon would take you across the River Styx to the world of the dead. In amphitheatres, men dressed as Charon would drag away the bodies as if they were taking them to the afterlife. If gladiators were fatally wounded, the men would finish them off with a hammer blow to the head.

I leant back against the wall to support my quaking legs. I wondered how I'd even manage to walk into the arena, let alone fight.

Rufus and Paulus went out next. I listened to their shouts and cries, convinced I was entering into the last few minutes of my life.

'Don't worry about it,' said Decimus. 'Just make sure you give the crowd a good death. I'll hold your head still and slit your neck. Make sure you don't scream, for the sake of your fans.'

I didn't think I'd have much choice. I cry when I stub my toe, so I doubted I'd be able to keep quiet while my throat was sliced open.

Decimus nudged me. 'We're on,' he said. 'Let's make it a good one.'

He strode out into the arena, lifting his sword and shield. There was a massive cheer from the crowd.

I stumbled after him and looked around. I'd never seen so many people before. There were twice as many in the amphitheatre as in the whole of Pompeii. My gaze flitted around spectators who were laughing, scowling, shouting, talking and eating. I wondered how many of them would keep munching throughout my death.

I lifted my trident and net with my shaking hands. There was a muted round of applause.

An announcer on the front row declared the start of the fight. I told myself that if I was to have any chance at all of winning, I'd have to take Decimus by surprise with a quick attack.

I told my legs to run forward. They took no notice. In fact, they did the opposite. I found myself running away.

Loud boos rang out. I could see people getting to their feet, pointing at me and yelling.

'That's sneaky even for you, Cassius!' shouted a man on the front row.

I wanted to tell him that it wasn't my fault. I'd told my legs to go forward, but they'd gone the other way.

I glanced over my shoulder and saw that Decimus was still standing with his feet spaced apart and his dagger held up. He shrugged and chased after me.

I told my legs to stop. I was going to die anyway, so what difference would a few extra minutes make? This way I'd die a coward and get endless hassle from the Furies in the next world.

'Come and fight!' yelled Decimus. 'You're ruining it for everyone!'

It was no use. I just kept going, circling around with Decimus following.

The crowd were jeering and hissing. A hunk of stale bread landed just in front of me, which had no doubt been aimed at my head.

I cut across the centre of the arena, and felt something wobble under my feet. I glanced down and saw it was one of the trapdoors they use to spring out dangerous animals in the beast shows. I could hear a lion roaring beneath it.

The door had dented where I'd stepped and I thought how lucky I was that it hadn't given way. I'd have crashed down to the level below and been torn apart by the hungry beast. It would have been an even worse death than the one I was about to get.

Then I had an idea that was so good it almost made me stop and consider it. But stopping wasn't a very good idea, so I weighed it up as I fled.

I decided to try it. After all, I had nothing to lose.

I let Decimus get so close he could almost reach me with his sword. Then I led him into the centre of the arena and leapt onto the wobbly trapdoor.

The wood broke beneath my feet as I sprung onto it. I found myself flopping forward onto

the hot sand just ahead of it. If Decimus had still been behind me, I'd have been dead. But he wasn't there. He'd crashed down through the broken trap door and into the pit below.

I pushed myself back up and went over to have a look. Decimus was rolling around, holding his knee and screaming. There was another shape down there too. A furry, snarling shape. It pounced and fixed its jaws around his neck.

I closed my eyes and tried to block out the noises of Decimus shrieking and the lion feeding.

I looked up at the announcer, who was hunched over, trying to peer down the trapdoor.

'Cassius wins, I suppose,' he said.

There were a few boos from the crowd, but most of them made no noise at all.

I sloped back to the corridor, where I found
Lucius frowning and shaking his head.

'You were meant to die,' he said. 'Why
didn't you?'

'Sorry,' I said.

'This is a disaster,' he said. 'I've lost one of
the best fighters, another has become a coward,
and the crowd weren't even entertained. No one
will ever want to use my fighters again.'

He led me and the others back down the dark
corridor to the school. I was so stunned about
being alive I couldn't speak. I'm still pretty
shocked now.

April XX

All the other surviving gladiators had to have their wounds treated by a doctor today, but there was nothing for me to do but sit on my straw and think about what happened.

I wondered if I should feel guilty for guiding Decimus to the trapdoor. Probably not. He was trying to kill me, after all. And he seemed very laid back about dying in battle anyway. Though he might have wanted a more heroic death than being a lion snack, I suppose.

'I don't know what to do about you,' said Lucius when he dropped off my morning porridge. 'I can't send you into the arena again. The whole city is angry about what you did.'

'Then let me go,' I said. 'There's no point in keeping me if I'm no use to you.'

'But I spent so much on you,' he said. 'It seems like such a waste.'

He shook his head and closed my door again. I couldn't believe I was trapped just because of the price he'd paid for me. What difference did it make now anyway?

Lucius looked much more cheerful when he came back with my lunchtime porridge.

'I've finally worked out what to do with you,' he said.

'Thanks so much,' I said, leaping to my feet and heading for the door. 'You've definitely made the right decision.'

He held his thick arm out to block the doorway.

'I'm not letting you go,' he said. 'I've

arranged for you to fight a murmillo called
Brutus in three days. He belongs to another
lanista, so I won't make as much money, but I
think it's the right thing to do. He'll give you a
good death, and the crowds will forgive me for
what happened yesterday.'

I slumped back down on my pile of straw.

'Oh,' I said. 'Do I need to go out there and train?'

'There's no point,' said Lucius. 'Brutus is
one of the best fighters in Rome. You'll be dead
whatever you do. But the crowd are going to
love it. It will be magnificent.'

He strolled away, whistling to himself.

So it turns out that all the effort I'd put into not
dying wasn't really worth it. All it got me was a
few extra days.

Oh well. Maybe I can be braver this time and get into a better part of the afterlife.

April XXI

Lucius let me out of my cell today to watch the others train. It was nice to get out of my smelly room for one of my last-ever days.

I sat on the wooden seats with Sextus and Claudia while Rufus and Paulus fought. Rufus is a Thracian, who uses a small, curved sword, and Paulus is a hoplomachus, who has a round shield, heavy helmet and spear. They were going through their moves with wooden replicas of these weapons while we looked on.

I was surprised to see how much thought they put into their battles in advance. I'd always assumed gladiators were just thugs who bashed away at each other, but I suppose there's more to it than that.

Claudia leaned over and poked me in the ribs. She fixed her pale blue eyes on me and grinned.

'I'm surprised you're showing your face after what you did to Decimus,' she said. 'I always thought you were a coward, but even I didn't expect that.'

I sighed. I thought about telling the truth, but I didn't have the energy to try any more.

'I got a bump on the head,' I said. 'And it made me forget how to fight.'

Claudia folded her arms and leaned towards me.

'Are you sure that's not just an excuse for turning chicken?' she asked.

'It's true,' I said. 'I don't remember any of my training. I don't remember who anyone is. I don't even remember why we have a girl like you fighting alongside us.'

Sextus winced and buried his face in his hands.

Claudia pounced up and pressed her wooden sword against my throat.

Just watch it, okay?

'Is that a problem?' she asked.

'No,' I said in a high, squeaky voice. 'I just thought it was unusual.'

I tried to move back along the seats, but Claudia grabbed the back of my head. I wondered if she'd need both hands to rip it off or if she could do it with one.

'But now I see it isn't unusual at all,' I said. 'I don't know why I even mentioned it.'

'Careful with him,' said Sextus. 'Lucius wants the little sneak to die in front of a crowd, remember. He thinks he can win back the favour of the public that way. He won't like it if you kill him now.'

Claudia stared at me and snorted out loud, fast

breaths. Then she tucked her wooden sword back into her belt and went back to yelling at Rufus and Paulus as if nothing had happened.

I slumped back on my seat and picked splinters out of my neck. I'd been spared, which meant I could live for two whole extra days. Whoopee.

GET REAL

Some gladiators were female, though it was rare. A few records mention women taking part in battles, and a sculpture discovered in Turkey shows two female gladiators in combat.

April XXII

Today I sat with Rufus and Paulus and watched Claudia and Sextus fight. Sextus is a Samnite, with a short sword, a shield and a row of feathers on the top of his helmet. He's a strong, fast fighter, but Claudia is even better.

I chatted to Paulus while we were watching them, and at one point I asked him how he'd ended up being owned by Lucius. I was amazed to discover he wasn't a slave or a prisoner at all. He'd actually volunteered to be a gladiator.

He said he always admired the heroes of the arena, and his ordinary life seemed dull by comparison, so he agreed to join Lucius's troupe.

He reckons it was worth giving up his freedom for the excitement and glory of his new life.

He knows he won't live as long, but he has plenty of adoring fans, and women who wouldn't have glanced at him before now chant his name.

What must his life have been like before for him to choose this nightmare?

GET REAL

Gladiators were mostly slaves and prisoners who were bought and trained by a lanista. But some volunteered. They might have needed money, wanted to become famous, or simply been drawn to the danger. There was even an emperor, called Commodus, who fought in the battles, though he only took part in ones he was guaranteed to win.

April XXIII

So this is it. The final day of my life. Again.

I've just been reading back over my scroll, as there's nothing else to do in my room. I notice that early on I wrote that I'd rather be in danger in Rome than bored in Pompeii.

I take it all back, of course. I'd love to be hanging around in Pompeii right now instead of terrified in this reeking cell. I'd savour the boredom like a seven-course meal.

So I suppose I can't criticise Paulus for wanting a risky life when I felt just the same way.

I don't know why I'm still writing so small on this scroll. It's not like I'll ever need to use the rest of it.

Goodbye. Hope those afterlife judges aren't too strict with me.

April XXIV

Yep. Still alive. I survived again. Glad I kept all this free space on the scroll now.

I stepped out into the arena last night to deafening boos.

'The disgraced retiarius Cassius returns!' yelled the announcer.

The boos grew even louder.

'And finishing him off tonight, we have the murmillo Brutus!' shouted the announcer.

Now cheers rang out.

At the other end of the arena was the biggest man I'd ever seen. In fact, he was one of the biggest things of any species I'd ever seen, and I helped Dad choose an ox once.

He was perhaps seven feet tall and almost as wide. I wondered how his owner managed to fit him in one of the tiny gladiator rooms. He had a short sword, a long shield and a bronze helmet that covered his face.

He lifted his sword up and the crowd chanted, 'Kill him, Brutus!'

He had huge muscles and tanned skin that was broken up by scars. He looked so solid that I doubted my trident would do much damage even if I got near him. It would probably just buckle on impact.

I couldn't win. The best I could hope for was to die without embarrassing myself.

Brutus stomped towards me.

I shouted 'Elysium here I come!' and told my legs to charge at him. This time they obeyed. To my surprise, I kept on running with my trident held out.

I was expecting Brutus to run at me too, but he did something very odd instead. He dropped his sword and shield on the ground and grabbed his chest.

I wondered if this was a clever tactic to throw me off my guard. If so, it was a very odd one. He was staggering around in circles and wheezing.

'I can't breathe,' he said. Sweat was pouring from the bottom of his visor.

'Do you still want to have the fight?' I asked. 'I can wait for you to get your breath back if you like.'

'I'm dying,' he gasped. 'Don't let me do it like this. Not in front of the fans.'

He collapsed to the ground and pointed at his chest. 'Strike me here,' he whispered. 'Let me die a hero.'

I stood above him and drew my trident back. There were no chants of 'Kill him!' from the crowd, just a low murmur of conversation. They were just as confused about what was happening as I was.

'Are you sure you want me to do this?' I asked.

'Yes…' he rasped.

I tried to bring my arm down and plunge the trident into him, but I just couldn't do it.

'Okay,' I said. 'Last chance to change your mind.'

His whole body was shaking and foamy saliva was running out of his visor along with the sweat.

'That's it,' I said. 'I'm definitely going to do it now.'

Brutus fell still. His right hand rolled off his chest and flopped into the sand. I slammed my trident into the gap between his arm and his body to make it look like I'd finished him off, then I planted my foot on his chest and held my arms up in victory.

There was nothing from the crowd but a few awkward coughs.

The man who was meant to be Charon shuffled out and grabbed Brutus's right ankle. He tried to drag the body over to the side of the arena, but it was too heavy, so I had to help him.

By the time we'd lugged it over there, most of the crowd were filing out of their seats. Once again, I'd ruined their entertainment.

As we plodded back down the corridor to our rooms, Rufus tapped me on the shoulder.

'I know how you're winning, Cassius,' he said. 'There's a curse on you. It will bring bad luck to everyone around you. I think Lucius should release you before it affects the rest of us.'

'That would suit me fine,' I said. 'Tell Lucius all about the curse if you like. As long as I'm set free, I don't care why.'

April XXV

Lucius was scowling when he came in with my porridge this morning.

'They say you've had the evil eye cast on you,' he said. 'And that you'll bring bad luck to everyone around you. Is that true?'

Grrrrr...

'Yes,' I said. 'Well, not really. But I'm happy to go along with it if it means I'll be set free.'

Lucius stared down at my straw and shook his head.

'It makes sense,' he said. 'I've had terrible fortune since you had your funny turn. First you kill one of my best fighters, then you kill one of the best fighters in Rome. The crowd hate me now. They won't want to see any of my troupe back in the amphitheatre any time soon.'

It did sound pretty bad when he put it like that.

'You should probably release me before I bring you any more misfortune,' I said.

'No,' said Lucius. 'I've already explained this. I paid too much for you. Getting rid of you would be like throwing coins into the dirt of the street. It's unthinkable.'

He closed the door, leaving me with just my porridge and this scroll for company. So it looks like I'll be stuck in this tiny room forever. Maybe I'll end up wishing that murmillo had finished me off after all.

GET REAL

Like many ancient cultures, the Romans believed a glance known as 'the evil eye' could place a curse on someone. It would lead to bad luck, injury and even death.

Chapter 4

Going on tour

April XXVI

I had some good news today. No, I haven't been set free. But I will at least be getting out of this tiny room.

Lucius thinks the people of Rome hate him now, so he's agreed to take the troupe on a tour of amphitheatres in smaller towns.

Rufus has convinced him I'm cursed, so he doesn't want any of the others to fight me. But I've still got to go along because I belong to him.

Doesn't sound too bad. I get to sit in the back of a cart and see some new places, and I won't even have to get hacked into pieces when I reach them.

April XXVII

We set off first thing this morning. Lucius led me out to his cart and chained my legs so I couldn't run away. The cart is covered at the sides and the front, but open at the back. It's pulled by two horses, and there's a seat on top for Lucius. The rest of us sit facing each other inside.

The others were already in when I arrived, which meant I could sit at the back and get the best view.

Everyone scowled and tutted at me as I got in. They seem annoyed about leaving Rome, and I know they blame me for it.

The streets were quiet at dawn, and the city looked very different. I was hoping we might go past Uncle Quintus's house so I could shout for his help, but we went the opposite way.

We climbed a hill to the east, and I got a great view of the forum in the pink morning light.

Sextus leaned over and pointed down at the city.

'That's where we should be fighting,' he said. 'Not in some pathetic little backwater.'

'I didn't give up my freedom for this,' muttered Paulus. 'I wanted to fight in the greatest city on earth, not some town nobody's heard of.'

I was going to point out that if you give up your freedom, you can't really complain about where you go, but I thought it might be a bad moment. I'll wait until the others have simmered down a little before I offer that sort of advice.

April XXVIII

We arrived in the town of Antium tonight, and Lucius showed us to our rooms in the local gladiator barracks. Mine is much bigger than the one in Rome, so I was already quite pleased with how things were going.

Less than an hour later, Lucius unlocked the door. I thought he was going to give me some bread or porridge, but he actually took us all to a party at one of the grandest houses in the town.

Young children lined our route, cheering and holding up small bronze figures of gladiators. One boy thrust a retiarius figure at me and yelled, 'Cassius will win!'

I felt bad that I wouldn't be taking part in the games, but at least the boy wouldn't have to see his hero screaming and running away.

Inside the house, we lay on couches while slaves brought us plates of eggs, fish and dormice.

Being a gladiator is weird. You're as low as the commonest slave, yet more famed and loved than any free man.

I watched Paulus entertaining the local women with tales of his violent victories and I remembered him saying that no one used to take any notice of him. It helped me understand a little better why he gave up his freedom.

I even found myself inventing stories about fights for the locals who flocked around me. I quite enjoyed it, but now I'm back in my room I feel guilty. It's nice to have all this attention, and I've certainly never known anything like it before, but I wish I'd done more to deserve it.

April XXIX

Lucius let me watch the games with him today. Before our fighters went on, some local gladiators had a battle. I can see why they need to hire proper ones from Rome, because these ones were dreadful.

They weren't gladiators at all, really. They were just prisoners who had been handed armour and weapons and thrown into the arena. I watched as they stumbled around, randomly hacking and slashing. They were so terrible that even I would have stood a chance against them.

I watched as one of them rushed forward to stab another with a curved sword. He tripped over and cut himself instead.

Soon most of them were rolling around in the sand and clutching their wounds. A hairy man

dressed as a Thracian planted his foot on the chest of one of the fallen fighters and glanced at Lucius.

Lucius scowled and shook his head. The man's hairy shoulders slumped.

'What was that about?' I asked.

'Sometimes a lanista will spot talent in an amateur bunch like this,' said Lucius. 'They'll buy them for their troupe and train them up.'

Over on the sand, a man with a dirty toga draped over his head, who was probably meant to be Charon, was dragging bodies away.

'I won't be forking out for any of this lot,' said Lucius. 'My horses could use the weapons better than they did.'

'Is that how you found me?' I asked. 'In one of these mass brawls?'

Lucius folded his arms and peered at me.

'You really don't remember a thing, do you?' he asked. 'No, I bought you at a slave auction. For far too much, it turns out. I should have haggled for longer.'

A small trumpet parped, and Rufus and Paulus rushed out. There was a loud cheer and everyone on the front rows stood up to shout advice and encouragement. The young children on the top seats leapt up and waved small Thracian and hoplomachus figures.

As soon as they began to fight, you could tell they were proper gladiators and not the ridiculous chancers we'd just been watching.

Instead of the heavy plodding of the amateurs, Rufus and Paulus moved quickly and skilfully. Rufus would jab his sword with awesome speed, and Paulus would bring his shield around to meet it just as quickly. Paulus would thrust his spear out, but Rufus would leap back, just escaping its sharp tip.

I found myself edging forward on my seat, desperate to find out who'd win. For a few minutes, I forgot all about the misery of the last few weeks, and I was caught up in the fight.

Eventually Rufus forced Paulus to the ground, crouched on his chest and held his sword against his throat.

It was all over. Rufus had won. Now Paulus's fate was up to the crowd.

Except that it wasn't really. Lucius had agreed with the local governor, who was in charge of the fight, that none of his fighters would be killed. He wasn't going to waste any of his famous gladiators on a small town like this.

Paulus threw his shield and spear aside, got on his knees and held his finger up to the governor.

'Kill him!' chanted the crowd. 'Kill him!'

The governor stroked his chin, as if considering it.

'Let him live!' he cried. 'He has fought well.'

There was a groan from the crowd. Paulus got up and walked off, with the crowd yelling abuse at him.

They soon forgot their anger as Sextus and Claudia came out to battle.

This fight was even more exciting than the last one, and for a while it looked like Claudia was going to lose. Sextus slashed her thigh, and she fell to the ground, wincing and biting her lip. But she managed to stagger up, and soon it was Sextus who was lying in the sand. Claudia pressed the tip of her sword into his neck, drawing a small trickle of blood.

Sextus threw his sword aside and begged the governor for mercy. Again, he pretended to consider it before letting him go.

There were more boos from the crowd, but they seemed happy enough as they filed out. I could hear them going over the highlights, acting out the best moves and discussing tactics.

I enjoyed watching the fights today much more than I had in Rome. And not just because I didn't have to face certain death afterwards. I'm beginning to understand the difference between experienced fighters like Rufus, Paulus, Sextus and Claudia, and clueless thugs like the prisoners who went on first.

There's a lot of skill to this sport. Maybe Septimus and Marina were right about it all along.

April XXX

Seeing as though I'm stuck here, I'm wondering if I should ask the others to train me as a gladiator. It's not like I want to actually take part in the battles or anything, but it might be fun to learn.

Also, it might make me feel a little less guilty about all the attention I'm getting from fans. At least if I can fight a little, I won't feel too bad about them treating me like a hero.

And it would mean I could be let out of my room in the daytime like the others. I'll ask Lucius tomorrow.

May 1

Well that didn't go very well. Lucius opened my door to give me some bread and water this morning, and I stuck my foot in the door.

'Could I come out and talk to you?' I asked. 'I've had an idea.'

He nodded and I led him over to the courtyard, where the wooden training weapons were piled.

'You remember how I forgot to fight after getting hit on the head?' I asked.

'Of course I do,' said Lucius. 'Every night I weep myself to sleep thinking of the money I've lost.'

'Right,' I said. 'Well I've thought of a way I could get my knowledge back again.'

I held the wooden trident out in front of me.

Lucius clapped his hands together.

'Of course!' he shouted. 'All I need to do is hit you on the head again just as hard, and you'll remember everything.'

'Yes,' I said. 'No. Wait. What?'

Lucius grabbed the wooden trident from my hands and swung it at my head. I ducked aside and ran.

'This isn't what I meant!' I shouted.

I fled around the courtyard, with Lucius following.

'Just let me hit you once!' he shouted. 'Then I can start making money from you again!'

It wasn't as hard to escape from Lucius as it had been from Decimus. I just kept going until he collapsed to the ground, sobbing and repeating the word, 'money'.

I collapsed next to him and got my breath back.

'Hitting me on the head won't give me my memory back,' I said. 'It will only damage me more. What I was going to suggest was that you get the others to train me, then I might remember how to fight.'

'I suppose so,' said Lucius, wiping a tear from his cheek.

He got to his feet and handed me the wooden trident. He let me swoosh it around in the air while he gazed silently at the sky, no doubt mourning the loss of all the coins he handed over for Cassius.

May 11

We were back in the cart today, on the way to our next stop, Tarracina. I thought I'd take the chance to see if the others would talk to me.

'I don't suppose any of you could help me remember my fighting skills, could you?' I asked. 'If you could train me like I was a complete beginner, maybe they could come back.'

'No,' said Sextus. 'You made us leave Rome for these silly little towns. We don't owe you anything.'

He slumped back against the far side of the far end of the carriage and scowled.

'It wasn't my fault that Brutus had a heart attack,' I said.

'It was your fault,' said Rufus, who was sitting opposite me. 'Because of the curse that's fallen on you. Training with you would only bring us more bad luck.'

'We haven't had any bad luck,' I said. 'We've all had quite a nice tour so far.'

Rufus leaned forward and fixed his gaze on me.

'I remembered something last night,' he said. 'A few years ago I spoke to an augur who told me I'd meet a tall man with short brown hair who would face a great disaster. Only now do I realise he was talking about you.'

'There are lots of tall people with short brown hair,' I said. 'And some of them are bound to be unlucky. That doesn't seem like much of a prediction.'

Rufus jabbed his finger at me.

'And that's not all,' he said. 'Just this morning, as we were leaving Antium, I heard a fig seller shouting 'Cassius will bring you bad luck!"

Paulus shook his head and tutted.

I heard this fig seller too, and I'm pretty sure what he was really shouting was 'half-price figs!'

This whole curse thing is total nonsense. But I have to admit it spooked me a little. Every time the cart went over a bump, I imagined it would overturn and we'd all die and it would be my fault.

GET REAL

The Romans were very superstitious, and saw hints about the future everywhere. Certain animals such as snakes and black cats were considered unlucky. An 'augur' would study the flight paths of birds for messages about things to come, and a 'haruspex' would do the same but with the entrails of dead animals. Yuck.

Chapter 5

⊢—⊣

Becoming a gladiator

May III

Lucius has stopped the cart at the side of the road so we can sleep for the night. I agreed to stay on guard for the first part of the night, but I didn't really see the point. Surely even the bravest thief wouldn't try to steal a cart full of gladiators.

I was gazing up the dark, deserted road when Sextus stepped out, clutching his sword.

Without saying a word, he walked over to a tree at the side of the road and began to attack it. I wondered what it had done to upset him so much.

'Pretty nasty tree, eh?' I asked.

'I have no opinion about it,' he said. 'But I do have a fight against Claudia tomorrow, which I intend to win. So while she sleeps, I'll train.'

He slashed at the trunk, cutting away a chunk of bark.

'Maybe you could show me how to do that?' I asked. 'It might help to bring my memory back.'

'No,' he said. 'You'll bring me bad luck if I agree to battle you.'

He thwacked the trunk again.

'But I wouldn't be battling you,' I said. 'I'd be battling the tree. And you've already said you don't care about that.'

Sextus peered at me for a moment, then shrugged.

'Fine,' he said. 'But just for a few minutes, then you need to leave me alone.'

He handed his sword over, and pointed at the tree. 'Battle away.'

I drew my arm back and bashed the sword into the tree. Pain shot up my arm and I shrieked.

'That was pathetic,' said Sextus. 'How has a bump on the head done this to you?'

He grabbed the sword and swung it into the side of the tree in a wide arc.

'You need big gestures,' he said. 'A gladiator battle is a performance, not a drunken brawl. The people in the top rows need entertaining too, even in these pathetic little towns we've ended up in thanks to you.'

He handed the sword back to me, took a step back and planted his hands on his hips.

I took a deep breath, pulled the sword back and swung it round in a huge circle. It clanged so heavily I had to drop it and clutch my shoulder.

'Ow!' I screamed.

'Amazing,' said Sextus. 'I know that bump changed you, but I still didn't think you could be beaten by a tree.'

May IV

I pointed out the tree to the others as we set off this morning.

'I battled that tree last night,' I said. 'And it doesn't seem to have suffered any bad luck. So that proves all that nonsense about my curse wrong.'

'We don't know what's going to happen to it next,' said Rufus. 'Someone could chop it down tomorrow and make every branch into a wiping stick. I bet if we stayed here for long enough we'd see some misfortune befall it.'

I wanted to tell him that something bad could happen to anything if you waited long enough. But there was no point. Rufus is convinced I'm cursed and he wouldn't have changed his mind if gold coins had started growing on the tree right in front of us.

GET REAL

The Ancient Romans didn't have toilet paper, so they used wiping sticks instead. If you were lucky, they would have sponges on the end. In public toilets, you would rinse the sponge and leave it for the next person to use. Eww.

The writer Seneca reported one of the weirdest suicides in history. He described a German gladiator who choked himself by stuffing one of these toilet sponges down his throat.

May V

We arrived at Tarracina this evening. The locals held another feast to welcome us, and I was enjoying the rich food after all the stale bread and dry figs we had on the journey.

But then one of the local girls came over to my couch and asked me who I'd be fighting. When I told her I wouldn't be fighting at all because I'd forgotten how to, she cut the conversation dead and went off to talk to Paulus instead.

I don't know why this annoyed me. I'm only here by mistake, and I'm not a real gladiator, so why should I care what anyone thinks?

I should be pleased that I'm disappointing Cassius's fans and earning him a reputation as a coward after what he did to me.

But the weird thing is, they're my fans now. I've

inherited them. And I wish I could be the brave hero they think I am.

I got Lucius to take me back to my room and I practised with my net and trident for over an hour. I had no idea how to use the weapons, but just leaping around with them made me feel a little better.

May VI

Our troupe were on after another load of prisoners again. This time they were meant to be recreating a battle from hundreds of years ago when Rome beat Hannibal's army, but you couldn't really tell. The two sides just stabbed away randomly at each other. If that's really how we fought back then, I'm amazed we're still around at all.

Once again, our gladiators made up for the

pathetic amateurs. First, Rufus and Paulus slogged it out for so long that the local governor declared them both winners. The crowd were surprisingly okay with this. They usually get upset when no one dies.

Then it was time for Sextus and Claudia. Despite all his practise on the tree, Sextus was well beaten. Claudia stabbed him in the chest and he fell to the ground with blood spurting through his fingers. The crowd leapt to their feet and chanted 'kill him!' This time Lucius got to his feet as well. I think he was worried that Claudia might have gone too far. But it turned out she'd missed his heart, and so he's still with us.

The local governor declared he'd fought well enough to be spared, and the crowd didn't even boo. Maybe they'd already seen enough blood to make the afternoon worthwhile.

GET REAL

Famous battles were re-enacted to entertain crowds in amphitheatres, with prisoners taking the place of soldiers. Some arenas were even flooded so sea battles could be staged.

May VII

We're staying in the gladiator barracks here in Tarracina for a couple of days while Sextus is treated by the local doctor, so I tried to get some more advice on fighting. I took my trident and net out to Rufus and Paulus, who were training in the courtyard.

'How did I use these when I was fighting against you?' I asked.

'Like a sneaky, cheating coward,' said Paulus.

I heard laughter from behind Rufus's helmet.

'Show me exactly,' I said. 'It will help me get my memory back.'

Rufus took his helmet off and ran his hand through his sweaty red hair.

'We're not going to train against you,' he said. 'Because of your curse.'

'This wouldn't be training against me,' I said. 'Just acting out what I used to do. That wouldn't be enough to set off my curse even if I had one.'

Paulus lifted his helmet off and placed it on the floor.

'I don't mind doing it,' he said. 'But don't be upset if you remember how much better than you I was.'

He picked up my trident and net.

'What would happen is I'd charge towards you and you'd back away and whimper with fright,' he said. He cowered behind the trident and made a high shrieking noise.

'Really?' I asked. 'But how was Cassius a successful gladiator if that's all he did? I mean if that's all I did?'

Paulus stared at me and scratched his cheek.

'You're serious, aren't you?' he asked. 'You don't even remember that?'

'No,' I said. 'It's all gone.'

He threw the net over his left arm and raised the trident with his right.

'You were a different type of gladiator from me,' said Paulus. 'So you fought in a different way. The crowds enjoy seeing how the various types of fighters do against each other. They like watching me because I'm the fastest and strongest.'

Rufus pretended to cough, but really he said the word, 'Rubbish'.

Paulus stomped over to Rufus and spat on his shield. He wiped his lips and turned back to me.

'With a net man like you, it's different,' he said.

He stepped back and forth while jabbing the trident out.

'This is what you do,' he said. 'You tire us out by moving around the arena. Your armour is lighter, so you can keep going for longer.'

Paulus hopped from side to side, dodging an imaginary opponent.

'But how could I ever win a battle that way?' I asked.

'You wouldn't against me,' said Rufus. 'But with someone like Paulus here, you keep going until he's exhausted, then you throw your net over his helmet, drag him into the sand and stab him with your trident.'

Rufus mimed the actions he was describing and I found myself copying them.

The more I think about these fights, the more I can see the appeal. You could be an expert

in all the different types of fighter, but there's still no real way of knowing which way things will go. Maybe a fighter like Paulus would burn out, letting a tactical battler like Cassius take advantage. Or maybe he'd land an early, brutal strike to beat the net man.

May VIII

While Paulus, Rufus and Claudia trained against each other today, I leapt around with my trident and net, fighting an imaginary opponent. None of the others said I was doing it wrong, or took much notice of me at all.

Every now and then I'd imagine landing a blow with my trident and hearing the roar from the crowd.

So am I seriously thinking about taking part in these battles now? I don't know. Those two fights in Rome were terrifying. Surely I'm not going to volunteer to go through that again?

On the other hand, I don't want to be just a passenger on this trip. I want to feel like I'm a proper part of the troupe. Maybe that's worth a few cuts and bruises.

May IX

Sextus is healing well, so now we're on the move again. His chest is bandaged and he's slumped against the back of the cart asleep. Lucius says the doctor in Tarracina did a great job, even if he charged too much, and soon Sextus's injury will just be another of his scars.

May X

We are in Capua now. As Lucius was taking me to my room in the local barracks, I noticed someone had carved graffiti on the door. It read, 'Cassius is the greatest gladiator in the world'. It's amazing that one of my fans found out I was coming, and made the effort to do that. I mean, one of Cassius's fans.

It inspired me to train right away, so I got Lucius to bring my weapons into my room. There wasn't enough space to practise running around, but I think I managed to get a little faster with the trident. I wonder how I'd do against the others now.

May XI

On the way back from watching the games tonight, I noticed the graffiti had been changed to 'Cassius is the greatest coward in the world'.

I wonder if the same fan changed it when they found out I wasn't fighting.

I really feel like I'm letting my fans down. I know that's stupid because they aren't even my fans anyway, but I can't help it.

Paulus and Rufus were both really good again today, but Sextus was terrible. He was really pale and slow, and I don't think he'd recovered enough from his injury. Claudia had him on the floor in no time, and the crowd booed for ages when he was spared.

He looked like he was in pain the whole time, and he kept gritting his teeth to stop himself screaming.

I'm sure I could do a better job than that. Maybe I'll ask Lucius if he'll include me in the next lot of battles.

GET REAL

People in Ancient Rome loved to write on walls. Hundreds of pieces of graffiti have been preserved on the buildings in Pompeii and Herculaneum, and they give us a glimpse into the everyday lives of ordinary Romans.

It turns out ordinary Romans were obsessed with gossiping and toilet humour, just as we are. Examples include 'Cornelia amatur ab Rufo' (Cornelia is loved by Rufus), 'Oppi, emboliari, fur, furuncule' (Oppius, you're a clown, a thief and a cheap crook) and 'Secundus hic cacat' (Secundus pooed here). This last one was written three times on the same door. That's a bit too much information, Secundus.

May XII

I spotted Claudia whacking her sword against
a wooden pole outside her room this morning,
and I lugged my weapons over.

'Can you show me how I used to fight?' I
asked. 'It's coming back to me a little, but it
would really help if you could act it out.'

She spat on my trident.

'I'd never be a retiarius,' she said. 'I won't
even pretend to be one. True Romans face
danger, they don't run from it.'

She grunted and struck the side of the pole.

'In that case, show me how you used to fight
against me,' I said. 'I'll act out what I used to do too.'

'Rufus said we shouldn't train with you,' she

said. 'Because of your curse.'

I glanced around. There was no sign of the others. Maybe I could get away with a small lie.

'He changed his mind,' I said. 'Because nothing bad has happened on the trip yet. In fact, he's already trained me himself.'

Claudia folded her arms and peered at me for a while.

'Okay,' she said, shrugging. She got into her starting position, with her shield back and her sword up. 'Show me what you think you did.'

This was great. I was finally getting some proper training from a fearsome fighter. I hopped around, jabbing my trident back and forth.

'That won't work,' said Claudia. 'You need to

choose your moment to strike. If you do it too soon, this will happen.'

She clanged her shield down onto my trident, driving it into the sand. I struggled to pull it free, but she whipped her sword around to my neck and held it there. I swallowed, and felt a bead of sweat trickle down my forehead.

'You don't have time to rescue your trident,' she said. 'Think again.'

She pulled her sword away but kept her shield in place.

I let my trident fall to the ground, then threw my net over her head.

'Good,' she said. 'Now I've got to drop my sword to free myself.'

She threw her sword down and lifted the net away.

'So now neither of us have our weapons,' she said. 'Or so you might think.'

I heard a rattling noise to my right. I turned and saw Rufus watching us through a gap above his door.

'Claudia!' he shouted. 'Why are you training with Cassius? Did you forget about his curse?'

'He told me you'd changed your mind,' she said. 'And that you'd already trained with him.'

'No chance!' yelled Rufus.

Claudia looked back at me with her nostrils flaring.

'As I was saying, you might think I don't have

a weapon,' she said. 'But remember I've still got this shield. It can still give you a nasty whack.'

As she said the last word, she brought her shield up and slammed it into my face. I tumbled down to the floor and whimpered.

She picked her sword up and went back to striking the wooden post.

'Thanks for the training,' I said, when the pain had died down enough for me to talk.

'No problem,' she said. 'And don't ever lie to me again.'

May XIII

There's a huge yellow and purple bruise on the left side of my face and it hurts when I eat or speak.

Claudia was sitting opposite me in the cart today, and spent the journey chatting as usual. You'd never guess she'd been the one who put the mark on my face.

It's weird. If one of my friends from back home like Septimus or Marina had injured me, I'd expect a very serious apology before I

considered speaking to them again. Yet Claudia was acting like nothing had happened.

And I suppose it hadn't, by her standards. Gladiators chop each other's arms off one day and make friends again the next.

That's just what it's like when you lead such a violent life. Stabbing someone in the heart is as normal for them as selling a jar of garum is for Dad.

If I'm going to become a proper member of this troupe and join in the fights, I'll have to get used to that sort of thing too.

Chapter 6

⊢⊣

Bruised and battered

May XIV

We've arrived in Caudium now, and I've just come back from a celebratory meal.

Sextus was on the couch opposite, and I noticed he wasn't eating much. He looked really pale, and kept wincing and clutching his side.

His stab wound is still very sore and red. It doesn't seem to be getting better, probably because he's been training instead of resting.

Between the third and fourth courses, Lucius went over to him for a discussion. As soon as Lucius pointed at the wound, I knew what they were talking about.

Without thinking, I leapt up and dashed over to them.

'I can fight tomorrow,' I said, 'if Sextus is too ill.'

Lucius flinched back.

'What are you talking about?' he asked. 'You can't fight, because of that knock on your head.'

'I've remembered how now,' I said. 'I'm ready again.'

Sextus stood up and shoved his face close to mine.

'This is a private conversation,' he said. 'And I'm fighting tomorrow, not you.'

'Really?' I asked. 'You don't look well enough to me.'

I gave his wound a prod. It was just a gentle tap, but it was enough to send him crashing back to his couch and grimacing.

Sextus grabbed a goblet from the table and

drew it back to throw at me.

Lucius jumped in between us.

'What did I do to deserve such unruly fighters?' he asked. 'After all that money I paid for the pair of you, too. I must be insane.'

He stroked the greasy strands on the back of his head for a moment, then pointed at Sextus. 'You can rest tomorrow.'

Then he span round and pointed at me. 'You can fight against Claudia.'

I threw my hands up in the air as if I'd just won a battle.

I'm not feeling quite so triumphant about it now, though. Claudia is a really scary fighter. What have I let myself in for?

May XV

Lucius came to fetch me early this afternoon,
and I waited with the others outside Caudium's
small wooden amphitheatre.

A bunch of prisoners went on first, and the
sounds of them hacking, stabbing, screaming
and gurgling didn't do much to calm my nerves.

Rufus and Paulus went on next. They fought for
ages, and the crowd got really into it, which was
good, as they didn't get much entertainment
from our battle.

The crowd were still on their feet as Claudia
and I ran into the arena.

I saw a few fans who looked about my age
on the top row, and I thought about what a

shock Septimus and Marina would get if they could see me. They were probably still playing gladiators back in the forum, totally unaware that I was doing it for real.

We started and I hopped around, trying to keep Claudia moving so I could tire her out. I kept my eyes fixed on her sword, ready to duck if she lashed out.

153

I stepped back a few paces, drawing her across the arena. The crowd booed, and I felt like pausing to explain that I was retreating because of tactics and not cowardice, and if they thought this was bad they should have seen me in Rome.

I heard a man behind me yell, 'I've seen sacred chickens who could fight better than you.' I resisted the temptation to look at him, keeping my focus on Claudia.

Claudia struck out. I surprised myself by bringing my trident up to meet her sword rather than ducking back. It clanged between two of the prongs and a muted cheer went up from the crowd.

Claudia looked surprised too. I felt like I'd done something unexpected and clever, and I needed to take advantage of it.

154

I tried throwing my net over Claudia. Bad move. She dodged aside and it fell on the floor. While I was staring at it, she wrestled her sword free.

Maybe I hadn't been so clever after all. Now I'd lost my net, and I'd have to battle on with just my trident.

Claudia lashed out again, and I met her blow with my arm guard. A jolt of pain shot up to my shoulder. It was painful enough to be hit on the one part of my body that was protected. What was it going to be like when her sword hit my flesh?

I kept moving, leading Claudia around the sandy floor. Her movements were getting slower, her breathing heavier and her cheeks redder. It was working.

It was time to strike. I stabbed my trident out,

and Claudia only just managed to bat it away with her shield.

The crowd were cheering my every move now. They really thought I was a proper gladiator.

I must have let myself get distracted by this. My concentration dipped for a second, and that was all Claudia needed. While I was looking at her sword, she swung her shield round and whacked me in the face.

It landed right on the bruise she'd created the other day. I dropped my trident and fell to the ground, howling with pain.

It's hard to remember exactly how the next bit happened. I was still crying in the sand and rubbing my cheek when a cold, numb feeling in my side shut down all my other thoughts.

A fresh wave of pain swept through me and I wondered if I was going to be sick.

I looked down and saw blood spurting out of the side of my chest. It was mixing with the sand to make a horrible kind of red mud.

Now that I look back, I can see Claudia was being nice. She gave me a shallow cut that would look gory for the crowd, but wouldn't do any real damage. But it was hard to understand that at the time.

I was screaming and the crowd were booing. I hadn't dealt with my pain like a noble Roman warrior. I'd cried like a baby.

A chant of 'finish him' rang out. I was amazed such a small crowd could make such a din.

I managed to scramble to my knees, clutching my injured side. I raised my left hand and held a finger up to the local governor.

He made a big show of looking around the crowd, as if weighting up their opinion. But then he ignored them and let me live anyway.

The crowd were so angry about this I had to hobble away before they took matters into their own hands and pelted me to death with their snacks. I shuffled out, and Lucius took me to my room.

'What's wrong with you?' asked Lucius. 'I've seen you take injuries that would kill other men, but now you make all that fuss over a little scratch?'

He pointed down at my wound. Seeing the fresh blood made me whimper again.

158

'It's a shame because you were starting to look like your old self before all that,' he said.

So that's good, I think. I can almost pass as a proper gladiator. But what am I meant to do about my screaming problem? I can't tell myself not to yell when I'm in terrible pain. It would be like jumping in the sea and telling myself to stay dry.

May XVI

Lucius brought a doctor called Cornelius to my room this morning. He rubbed a vinegary ointment into my wound. It really stung, and I couldn't stop myself from shrieking. Then he wrapped a long piece of cloth around my back and stomach.

'The gladiator's injury should heal fairly quickly,' said Cornelius. 'But there's nothing I

can do for his cowardice. Have you thought about getting rid of him and buying a braver one?'

'I spent far too much on him,' said Lucius. 'I can't abandon my poor investment now. And here I go, wasting even more money.'

He handed over a coin to the doctor, and for a moment he looked in even more pain than I was.

May XVII

My wound is mending well. That doctor might have been rude, but at least he knew what he was doing.

I'm resting in my room today, and listening to the others train outside. Despite the horrible pain I had to endure, I enjoyed my fight with Claudia, and I'll battle again if Lucius wants me to.

I'm starting to think I could make a pretty good gladiator if I could only stop myself whimpering all the time.

GET REAL

Gladiators were very valuable to their owners, and they got better medical attention than most free Romans. The famous doctor Galen worked in a gladiator school.

May XVIII

We're back on the road now. I sat at the front of the cart, leaning against the end so I could rest while my wound healed. Sextus was opposite, still clutching his chest.

He made me peel back my bandages to show him how my wound was doing, and he winced when he saw it. He said it would take weeks to heal, which sent me into a panic.

But then I realised he was just trying to put me off the next battle, so he could do it instead. Just for that, I'm going to make a big point of telling Lucius I feel better.

May XIX

We arrived in Aeclanum this afternoon, and I told Lucius I was ready to fight again as soon as we got here. Sextus leapt down after me and announced he was fit too.

Lucius made us stand next to each other while he compared our wounds. He pressed mine and I let out a high yelp. Then he pressed Sextus's wound. Sextus didn't make a sound, but tears streamed down his cheeks.

He pointed at Sextus. 'You're in pain, but you sound fine.'

He pointed at me. 'You're fine, but you sound in pain.'

'I don't know what I've done to deserve such terrible fighters,' he said. 'You go ahead and fight, Cassius. But if you keep up that silly squealing, word will spread, and nowhere will ever book us again. Even a small place like this.'

Sextus glared at me, like it was my fault he was ill. I wasn't even the one who stabbed him.

May XX

My room is so small I couldn't practise leaping back and forth this morning. I just had to lie down and work out my tactics for beating Claudia.

I thought about all the moves she might do and how I'd counter them, and I felt pretty

well prepared. It was only when Lucius came
to take me to the arena that he mentioned I'd
be fighting Paulus instead. All my confidence
drained away, and I tried to work out what I
needed to do to beat someone with a spear.

We waited in the corridor leading to the arena
floor, while a band of local prisoners filed past.
I didn't concentrate much as they battered each
other. I spent the whole time looking at Paulus
and rethinking my game plan.

The crowd let out a loud cheer and I peered into
the arena to see what had happened. There was
one huge prisoner left standing. He was still
swinging his sword around randomly while the
others lay injured or cowering in fright.

I was glad the crowd had got some decent
entertainment. That took the pressure off us a little.

We went out next. I started by scuttling backwards, which led to the usual boos. I was hoping Paulus would get frustrated and throw his spear at me. If I could duck it, I might be able to grab it and throw it back at him.

He didn't fall for it. He just kept pacing round, jabbing his spear when he got close enough.

This went on for a while, and the crowd grew quiet. They couldn't even be bothered booing. I needed to do something to make it interesting.

I held my trident out and charged at Paulus. He pushed it aside with his spear. For a while we clanged our weapons together as if they were long, blunt swords. I could hear conversations breaking out in the crowd. Our fight clearly wasn't holding their attention.

I leapt back and then ahead again, striking

Paulus. My trident hit his arm guard, knocking him down to the sand.

I stood over Paulus and held my weapon in the air. The crowd were cheering. Cheering for me.

'Finish him!' they chanted.

Something shocking flashed through my mind. I'd won. I'd taken part in an actual gladiator fight in an actual arena and I'd won.

I took my eyes off Paulus to look at the cheering crowd. This turned out to be a massive mistake. In the split second that I flicked my gaze up, Paulus managed to turn things around.

It happened so fast that I'm still not sure entirely what he did. But I think he brought his spear round to the backs of my ankles, and shoved his shield into my thighs, toppling me over.

Then he was on his feet, and the sharp tip of his spear was pressed against my neck. I'd gone from winner to loser in an instant.

'Finish him!' chanted the crowd again. These were the same people who'd been cheering me on to kill Paulus a few seconds ago. I supposed they just wanted to see someone getting killed, and they didn't care who it was.

I let my weapons go and Paulus slammed his foot down on my chest. He planted it right on the wound from my last fight, sending pain up and down my body. But guess what? I didn't scream.

I held my finger up for mercy, and the local governor said I'd fought well and I should be spared. The crowd sounded really angry. As far as they were concerned, I didn't fight well at all. The contest was dull, and I allowed myself to be tricked at the end.

But I feel pretty good about my fight, all in all. I came really close to winning, and I managed not to yell with pain. This might not be saying much, but that was my best battle so far.

Hello everyone.

May XXI

We all climbed into the back of the cart this morning, ready to go to our next stop. I got on first, taking my spot at the front so I could rest again.

There was a delay after we were all in, and I craned around to see what was going on. Lucius soon emerged with a huge man, whose hands

and feet were bound with rope. I recognised him as the final prisoner standing from the fight yesterday.

'This is Barnabas,' said Lucius. 'The newest member of our troupe. I paid a lot for him, so be careful with him.'

Barnabas climbed onto the end of the cart, and his weight made it lift up. We set off, and I could feel we were going slower than before. The horses sounded pretty annoyed too.

Claudia chatted to Barnabas, and I heard him reply in a surprisingly high voice. I found myself sniggering, but then I remembered how well he'd fought in the arena, and I forced myself to stop. It wouldn't be a great idea to get on the wrong side of him.

Barnabas was blocking most of the back of the

cart, so I couldn't look out at the road. Instead, I found myself closing my eyes and drifting off to sleep.

When I woke up it was dark and I was the only one left in the cart. Lucius bundled me out and into my room in the local gladiator barracks before I really knew what was going on.

He says I'm taking part in the battle the day after tomorrow. Now he has six gladiators in total, we can all fight. I'd better stop writing this and get training, then.

May XXII

Lucius brought me some stew this morning. As soon as I tasted it, I knew. There was garum in it. And not just any garum. This was Neptune's Choice Luxury Garum, the one that Dad makes. I was certain of it.

I wondered if Dad had passed through this town after he'd been to Rome, or if some trader had brought it out here. I was surprised to find hot tears running down my cheeks into the bowl.

'I was about to congratulate you on not screaming yesterday,' said Lucius. 'But as this

Sob, sob…

It's not that bad!

173

meal has just made you cry, I can see you aren't over your cowardice problem just yet.'

'Sorry,' I said, wiping my cheeks. 'I won't do it in the arena tomorrow, I promise. Who am I fighting?'

I remembered Barnabas standing over a pile of injured and trembling prisoners. I really hoped it wasn't him.

'Sextus,' said Lucius. 'He requested it himself.'

Hmm. Not sure how I feel about that. Sextus still doesn't look like he's fully recovered from his injury, so I should have a chance. But it's strange that he asked to fight me. I hope he isn't holding a grudge against me for taking his place in the last two battles. Maybe he's planning to take his revenge by killing me.

Chapter 7

Victory!

May XXIII

Sextus didn't kill me. In fact, I beat him. You'd think that winning a proper arena fight would be the biggest news of my day, but it's not even close. What happened afterwards was so weird I'm having trouble remembering anything else.

But let me see. Claudia and Rufus went on first. Claudia dropped her sword, and it looked like Rufus had won. But she managed to knock him to the ground with her shield, and she ended up claiming yet another victory.

Then it was the turn of Paulus and Barnabas. I was so glad Lucius didn't pit me against Barnabas. He's been kitted out as a murmillo, with a sword, a long, heavy shield and a helmet that looked big enough for an ox.

Paulus fought hard, but he might as well have been attacking a wall for all the difference it made. Barnabas grabbed the end of his spear and yanked it out of his hand. Then he charged into him with his shield and barged him onto the floor.

It was all over way too quick, and I think Lucius is going to have to train Barnabas in the art of showmanship. These crowds will have been looking forward to the games all week. They don't want the fight to be over before they've had a chance to settle into their seats.

I stepped out with Sextus next. After my last fight, I was determined to keep my eyes on him and ignore the crowd. And I managed it, even though their reaction was odd right from the start.

Rather than cheering or shouting, they were muttering to each other as though something weird was happening. I blocked it out. If I looked around to see what was going on, Sextus would take his chance.

I jogged around the ring, leading Sextus out.

Instead of booing like usual, the crowd clapped, and some of them even called out my name, though there was something odd about it I couldn't place.

I kept moving. My tactic was working. Sextus was panting behind his heavy helmet, and sweat was pouring down onto his chest.

I stabbed my trident forward, and he tried to duck aside. But he wasn't quite fast enough, and one of the blades cut his left shoulder.

Sextus slashed back with his sword, but I blocked it with my arm guard. The crowd seemed to like this. They all seemed to be on my side for once.

Sextus staggered back, looking unsteady. I wondered if his injury was still bugging him and whether Lucius should have let him fight at all.

180

Then I threw my net over his helmet and yanked him down. His shield crashed out of his hand and rolled across the floor. He tried to hack at my leg, but I stamped on his wrist. His sword fell away and I kicked it aside.

And that was it. This time there was no surprise comeback. I'd actually won a fight in an arena.

I listened out for the cries of 'finish him', but they didn't come. The crowd were chanting my name instead, but there was still something wrong about it.

Then I worked out what it was. It wasn't wrong. It was right.

They weren't chanting, 'Cassius'. They were chanting, 'Marcus'.

I looked around, focusing on the audience fully for the first time. Lucius was on the front row, and I recognised the man who was sitting next him too. It was Gaius, our old town governor. But what was he doing here?

Just along from them, I spotted Septimus and Marina. Why had they travelled so far just to watch the games?

And that's when I finally realised. They hadn't travelled at all. I was back in Pompeii. While I'd been sleeping in the cart, we'd travelled down familiar roads right back to my home.

I scanned around, searching for the faces I most wanted to see.

Then I saw them, climbing down from the stands into the arena. It was Mum and Dad.

I ran over and hugged them.

Lucius leapt down too, forcing himself between us.

'Stay away from the fighters!' he yelled to my parents. 'They are incredibly dangerous.'

'He's not dangerous,' said Mum. 'He's Marcus, my son.'

'It's true,' I said. 'This is what I was trying to tell you back in Rome.'

Lucius grabbed me by the neck and dragged me out of the arena.

'This is my Cassius, my gladiator,' cried Lucius. 'I paid a good price for him, and no one is going to steal him.'

He forced me all the way to my room in the gladiator barracks. I'm still here now, trying to take in what happened.

I'm home. And surely I'll be free soon. Lucius will have to believe my story now, won't he?

May XXIV

I was wrong. Lucius has managed to convince himself that the entire town is lying to him. He was fuming when he came in with my stew this morning.

'They're all in on it,' he yelled. His cheeks were red and his voice was raspy. 'This whole town wants to trick me into giving away my property with their silly stories. I bet they try it on everyone. As soon as I hand you over, they'll take you straight down to the slave auction and

have a good laugh about how they scammed Lucius. Well, it's not going to happen.'

'They're telling the truth,' I said. 'I'm Marcus. Your Cassius ran away in Rome. That's why I couldn't fight for so long. Not because I had a bump on the head, but because I'd never been trained at all.'

He slammed the door, locked it behind him, and walked away muttering the word, 'Thieves.'

So I'm still here in the barracks, just a short walk away from the house I've lived in all my life. I'm back home, but if we don't sort this out soon, I won't be here for very long.

May XXV

Lucius didn't come to see me until late this afternoon. I was worried he might just give me more stew and rant about thieves again, but this time he beckoned me outside.

We ended up in the forum, where a huge crowd had gathered. Septimus and Marina were there, along with Mum, Dad and Gaius.

'This trickster is refusing to pay me until I hand you over,' said Lucius, pointing at Gaius. 'But I won't even consider giving you to these people unless you prove your story to be true beyond all doubt.'

He planted his hands on his hips and stared at me.

'Off you go, then,' he said.

I looked at the familiar buildings all around me.

'Those are the forum baths,' I said, pointing to my right. 'Over there is the Sea Gate. If you walk that way, you get to the theatre. That building is the Temple of Jupiter.'

'That proves nothing,' said Lucius. 'This town is much like any other.'

I wondered what Lucius would count as evidence. That had seemed pretty solid to me.

Marina stepped forward and held her hand up.

'What's my name?' she asked.

'Marina!' I shouted.

Marina turned to Lucius and shrugged. 'That proves he's Marcus and not your gladiator,' she said. 'He couldn't have got that right unless we knew each other.'

'You're probably just pretending that's your name to trick me,' said Lucius. 'Bunch of small-town robbers.'

Septimus stepped forward.

'This should work,' he said.

He pointed to his thigh. 'What do I have right here?' he asked.

'A birthmark in the shape of a dagger,' I said.

Septimus lifted up his tunic to reveal the mark.

'That proves it,' I said. 'There's no way I could have known that.'

Lucius shrugged. 'A lucky guess,' he muttered.

I sighed. If Lucius wouldn't accept that as evidence, I doubted he'd be satisfied by anything.

There was a shuffling at the back of the crowd and I heard someone gasp. At first I couldn't make out what was going on, but then I realised and a huge grin spread across my face. There was no way Lucius could deny this.

A man I recognised as the governor of Aeclanum pushed through the crowd. And following him, with his wrists bound by rope, was Cassius. He was scowling, and still wearing the tunic he stole from me.

'I spotted one of your gladiators in our forum this morning,' said the governor. 'I guessed he must have escaped from you.'

Lucius looked at Cassius, then at me, then back at Cassius again. He ran his hands through his straggly hair.

'Yes, I think he did,' he said. 'Quite a long time ago, in fact.'

May XXVI

I'm back in my own bedroom now. When I woke up this morning, I was convinced the last two months hadn't actually happened, and it was all just something I'd imagined after eating too much garum. Then I saw the scar on the side of my chest and I knew it had all been real.

Everything was sorted out pretty quickly after Cassius turned up yesterday. Lucius said I was free to go, though I didn't notice him apologising.

Then he yelled at Cassius, and dragged him over to the barracks.

After that, the mob descended. People I barely recognised swarmed around, asking how I'd ended up as a gladiator.

I had to push through to get to Mum and Dad, and even when I did it was hard to speak to them without the others interrupting.

Dad told me he'd stayed in Rome looking for me for two extra weeks, before coming back here to see if I'd managed to return.

I told him how Cassius had tricked me and he said he'd warned me about the dishonest people in Rome. He'd actually warned me about thieves, not lookalikes who con you into fighting in amphitheatres, but never mind.

Even when we got back home, the crowd didn't leave me alone. They crammed into our atrium and I had to stand on a table and tell them all my story. They had millions of questions, and by the time it was all over I was more exhausted than after one of my battles.

I've spent most of today sleeping it off, and even just writing this has made me need another nap.

May XXVII

Lucius and the others have gone now. I spotted their cart passing through the forum on the way to the Sea Gate this morning and I rushed up to say goodbye.

Cassius was sitting at the front and looking very annoyed. Sextus was opposite him, and seemed just as glum. It can't have been great for him to find out I wasn't a real gladiator right after I beat him, I suppose. But the others were friendly, and Claudia even said I'd done well to learn so much so quickly.

'Enjoy your freedom,' said Rufus. 'I hope I was wrong about your curse. I'm not so sure, though.'

They set off and I stood and waved until they were out of sight.

It's weird that Rufus is still going on about that silly curse. I'm staying right here, while he's going off to fight as a gladiator. If anything, it's me who should be worried about him.

See you soon, Marcus!

May XXX

Life is finally getting back to normal again. I still get stopped in the street, but most people have heard my story now, and their curiosity is dying away.

There were some loud rumbles in the ground yesterday, so most people are talking about those instead.

I found myself back in the forum playing gladiators with Septimus and Marina again this afternoon. It's weird pretending to be an arena fighter when I've done it for real, but I prefer being poked with sticks to being stabbed with swords.

I've enjoyed being home again, but every so often I remember about my curse and I get worried.

It can't be right, can it? I'm back in my small, safe, quiet town now. I don't have to face any swords or daggers or spears. What danger could I possibly face here in Pompeii?

The End

Gladiators in Ancient Rome

Marcus's diary is set in 79AD, almost two thousand years ago. Romans were the most powerful people in the world back then, commanding an empire that stretched from Britain to Africa. They loved to watch violent gladiator battles, where trained fighters would clash in huge arenas.

Gladiator fights had their roots in funeral ceremonies, where criminals or slaves would fight in tribute to the person who'd died. But they soon developed into a separate form of entertainment.

Gladiator battles took place in public spaces such as marketplaces at first, but they became so popular that large venues were built to hold the crowds. In 80AD, a huge stone stadium was opened in the centre of Rome, which could hold 50,000 people. Originally known as 'the Flavian Amphitheatre', we now call it the 'Colosseum'.

Most gladiators were slaves, but some were volunteers lured by the thrill of combat and the chance of glory. And while the majority were male, there's evidence that women fought too.

There were several types of gladiators, and audiences loved to see them pitted against each other. They wore different armour, and used different weapons such as swords, spears, daggers, nets and tridents.

These gory spectacles were paid for by the politicians. They realised they would be popular with the public if they laid on the kind of violent entertainment they craved.

As well as gladiator fights, the crowds in amphitheatres would watch recreations of famous battles, and beast shows, in which prisoners would be torn to pieces by lions, tigers and bears.

How do we know about gladiators?

The sort of gladiators Marcus describes in his diary were famous two thousand years ago. So how do we know so much about them?

A lot of writing from Ancient Rome has survived, including letters, poetry and plays as well as historical accounts written by people such as Tacitus and Julius Caesar. Lots of rude graffiti has also been preserved on Roman walls.

Many buildings from Ancient Rome are still standing. The Colosseum, where gladiators battled for tens of thousands of bloodthirsty Romans, is partly intact. Millions of people visit it every year,

making it one of the most popular tourist attractions in the world.

We can also learn about ancient life by studying objects that have been discovered in ruins and dug up from the ground. Paintings and sculptures show us what gladiators looked like and how they fought. Some of the best depictions of gladiators come from mosaics, which are made from small pieces of coloured glass or stone that have been cemented into place.

Timeline

753BC

Rome is founded by twin brothers named Romulus and Remus, who were rescued by a wolf. Except it wasn't. That's a myth. The less exciting truth is that small settlements formed on the hills above the River Tiber around 1000BC, and these eventually grew into a city.

264BC

The first gladiator games are held, at least according to the Roman historian Livy. But he also trotted out the Romulus and Remus myth, so this might not be right.

70BC

A huge amphitheatre is constructed from stone in Pompeii around this time. It is still

Timeline

standing today, and attracts millions of visitors every year.

73BC-71BC

The gladiator Spartacus leads a rebellion of runaway slaves against the Roman army.

59AD

A riot breaks out in the amphitheatre in Pompeii, and games are banned there for the next ten years.

72AD

Construction begins on the Colosseum in Rome, known then as the Flavian Amphitheatre.

Timeline

79AD

Mount Vesuvius erupts, showering Pompeii with ash and pumice, and killing around 2,000 people. The town lies preserved for 1,500 years, when the first excavations begin.

80AD

The Colosseum in Rome is opened by the emperor Titus. It is the largest amphitheatre in the empire, holding around 50,000 people.

404AD

The emperor Honorius issues a decree to stop gladiator fights.

410AD

Rome is attacked by the Visigoths, led by King Alaric. This is known as 'the sack of

Timeline

Rome' and was a key event in the fall of the Roman Empire.

2016

The first public performance since 79AD is held at the amphitheatre in Pompeii. But rather than a violent battle, it's a concert by rock star David Gilmour from the famous band Pink Floyd.

Gladiator Hall of Fame

Not much evidence survives about individual gladiators, but we do know the names of some from sources like graffiti in Pompeii and the poetry of Martial. However, some gladiators such as Spartacus had an impact far beyond the arena.

Carpophorus

Famous bestiarius, a type of fighter who was pitted against deadly wild animals. It's surprising any of them lived long enough to become well known, but Carpophorus managed it. The poet Martial describes how he killed twenty beasts in a single day and compares him to the mythical hero Hercules.

Celadus

Gladiator who fought in the Thracian style, with a small shield and short sword. We only

Gladiator Hall of Fame

know about him from graffiti scratched into the barracks at Pompeii. It tells us that he won three victories and was a heart-throb for all the girls. Let's face it, he probably wrote it himself, but let's give him the benefit of the doubt and include him in this hall of fame anyway.

Commodus

Roman Emperor who shocked the public by becoming a gladiator himself. He took part in arena battles dressed as a secutor, though the fights were fixed so he always won. But while he was in no real danger in the arena, he was in plenty of trouble in the real world. He was deeply unpopular, and was assassinated in 192AD.

Gladiator Hall of Fame

Crixus

Gladiator who led a slave revolt alongside Spartacus. Their rebellion grew into a series of battles that became known as the Third Servile War. When Spartacus heard about Crixus's death in 72AD, he sacrificed 300 Roman soldiers in his honour.

Flamma

Celebrated gladiator whose amazing record is written on his gravestone. He fought 34 times, won 21, drew 9 and lost just 4. He was dedicated to the life of combat, and although he was offered his freedom four times, he always refused it. He chose to keep battling in the arena until he was eventually killed.

Gladiator Hall of Fame

Hermes

Gladiator who lived in the first century AD and inspired Martial to write a poem. It describes how Hermes was better than all the other fighters, and could use a wide variety of weapons.

Marcus Attilus

We know about this successful gladiator from graffiti discovered in Pompeii. He seems to have been a free man who volunteered to fight. Although he was an inexperienced young fighter, he beat several famous gladiators such as Hilarus and Recius Felix. These surprise results inspired one of his fans to scratch drawings of his victories onto a tomb.

Priscus and Verus

Gladiators who fought in the opening day games at the Colosseum. According to the poet Martial, they fought an epic battle before putting down their swords at the same time in a show of respect. The emperor Titus declared them both winners and rewarded them with their freedom.

Spartacus

Gladiator who led a rebellion against his owner. He broke out of gladiator school, along with seventy other fighters. They made for Mount Vesuvius, where thousands of escaped slaves joined them. They fought off the Roman army six times, until they were finally beaten in 71BC. Spartacus remains the most famous gladiator of all.

Spiculus

Gladiator who fought in the first century AD. He was a favourite of the Emperor Nero, who gave him lavish gifts of property and slaves. A glass cup bearing his image was discovered in France, which shows how far his fame spread.

Glossary

Amphitheatre
A large circular or oval building in which gladiators battled.

Atrium
The main hall of a Roman house. The middle of the ceiling was open to the sky, with a small pool of water underneath.

Bestiarius
A professional fighter who battled wild animals rather than other humans.

Forum
A large public space in a Roman town surrounded by shops, offices and temples. It was the political, legal and social centre of a town.

Furies
Spirits of vengeance, according to Roman mythology. They tortured the damned in the underworld, but could also punish living people who'd done things like murdering members of their family.

Gladiator
Someone who took part in violent and often deadly fights for the entertainment of large crowds.

Gladiatrix
A female gladiator. An image of gladiatrices discovered in Turkey shows women fighting with daggers, shields and arm guards.

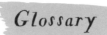

Glossary

Hoplomachus
A gladiator who fought with a spear and round shield.

Lanista
Someone who owned and trained gladiators.

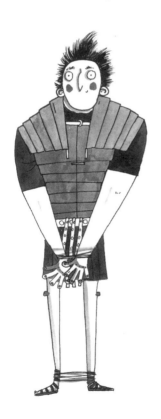

Loincloth
A strip of wool or linen worn around the waist to create an ancient version of underpants.

Murmillo
A gladiator who fought with a short sword, rectangular shield, arm guard and a visor covering their face.

Retiarius
A gladiator who fought with a trident, net and little armour.

Samnite
A gladiator who fought with a short sword and rectangular shield. Samnites were inspired by warriors from the Samnium region of Italy.

Glossary

Secutor
A gladiator who fought with a dagger, a curved shield and a helmet that covered their face.

Slave
A person who is owned by another person and forced to work for them.

Thracian
A gladiator who fought with a curved sword, small shield and a broad helmet with a visor.

Toga
A heavy piece of cloth worn as an outer garment. People often think of them as the typical clothing in Rome, but they were uncomfortable and worn mainly on formal occasions.

Tunic
A loose garment that was commonly worn in Ancient Rome. It was made from two rectangles of wool that were sewn together and fastened with a belt.

THE LONG-LOST SECRET DIARY OF THE WORLD'S WORST

Shortlisted for the
Lancashire School Library Service
Fantastic Book Awards (FBA) 2017–18.

'*Although easy to read, the vocabulary is
great and the plot lines engaging – excellent
reads for developing readers.*'
Library Girl and Book Boy Blog

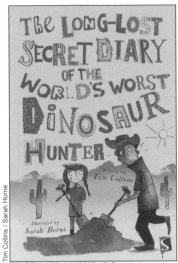

PB ISBN: 978-1-912233-19-9

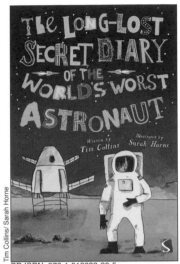

PB ISBN: 978-1-912233-20-5

PB ISBN: 978-1-912006-67-0

PB ISBN: 978-1-912006-66-3

A selected list of Scribo titles

The prices shown below are correct at the time of going to press. However, The Salariya Book Company reserves the right to show new retail prices on covers, which may differ from those previously advertised.

Gladiator School by Dan Scott

1	Blood Oath	978-1-908177-48-3	£6.99
2	Blood & Fire	978-1-908973-60-3	£6.99
3	Blood & Sand	978-1-909645-16-5	£6.99
4	Blood Vengeance	978-1-909645-62-2	£6.99
5	Blood & Thunder	978-1-910184-20-2	£6.99
6	Blood Justice	978-1-910184-43-1	£6.99

Iron Sky by Alex Woolf

| 1 | Dread Eagle | 978-1-909645-00-4 | £9.99 |
| 2 | Call of the Phoenix | 978-1-910184-87-5 | £6.99 |

Children of the Nile by Alain Surget

1	Cleopatra must be Saved!	978-1-907184-73-4	£5.99
2	Caesar, Who's he?	978-1-907184-74-1	£5.99
3	Prisoners in the Pyramid	978-1-909645-59-2	£5.99
4	Danger at the Circus!	978-1-909645-60-8	£5.99

Ballet School by Fiona Macdonald
1. Peter & The Wolf   978-1-911242-37-6   £6.99
2. Samira's Garden   978-1-912006-62-5   £6.99

Aldo Moon by Alex Woolf
1 Aldo Moon and the Ghost
    at Gravewood Hall   978-1-908177-84-1   £6.99

The Shakespeare Plot by Alex Woolf
1 Assassin's Code   978-1-911242-38-3   £9.99
2 The Dark Forest   978-1-912006-95-3   £9.99
3 The Powder Treason   978-1-912006-33-5   £9.99

Visit our website at:

www.salariya.com

All Scribo and Salariya Book Company titles can be ordered from your local bookshop, or by post from:

The Salariya Book Co. Ltd,
25 Marlborough Place
Brighton
BN1 1UB

My Secret
Diary

www.randomhousechildrens.co.uk

Jacqueline Wilson

My Secret Diary

Dating, Dancing, Dreams and Dilemmas

Illustrated by Nick Sharratt

CORGI BOOKS

MY SECRET DIARY
A CORGI BOOK 978 0 552 56156 3

First published in Great Britain by Doubleday,
an imprint of Random House Children's Publishers UK

Doubleday edition published in 2009
Corgi edition published in 2010

5 7 9 10 8 6

RANDOM HOUSE CHILDREN'S PUBLISHERS UK
61–63 Uxbridge Road, London W5 5SA

www.randomhousechildrens.co.uk

Addresses for companies within The Random House Group Limited
can be found at: www.randomhouse.co.uk/offices.htm

THE RANDOM HOUSE GROUP Limited Reg. No. 954009

A CIP catalogue record for this book is available
from the British Library.

The Random House Group Limited supports The Forest Stewardship
Council® (FSC®), the leading international forest-certification organisation.
Our books carrying the FSC label are printed on FSC®-certified paper. FSC is
the only forest-certification scheme supported by the leading environmental
organisations, including Greenpeace. Our paper procurement policy can be
found at www.randomhouse.co.uk/environment

Printed in the UK by CPI Group (UK) Ltd, Croydon, CR0 4YY

To Chris

The STORY SO FAR...

We just have to flap our wings and fly!

Wheee!

I invented imaginary games with my dolls when I was little.

Neigh! Come and ride on my back.

Hello horsey!

I played pretend games, even as a baby.

And when I was big.

I hate our stepmother!

Let's run away!

I played with paper dolls.

I love your evening gown!

Oh darling, wait till I tell you about the party!

I wish we didn't have to go to school today.

Still, at least we can play together at dinner time.

Sometimes my pretend friends were invisible.

Might I have the honour of a dance, fair lady Christina?

Certainly, my Lord Jack.

I had real friends, too – and sometimes we all played pretend games.

Some of my teachers liked me having a vivid imagination.

Some of my teachers found it tiresome.

My family weren't too thrilled, either.

I longed to write my own books. I wrote short stories and poems and plays and I started many, many 'novels'.

Then in 1960, the year I was fourteen, I started keeping a diary.

1
My Diary

I've kept a diary on and off all my life. When I was a little girl I had small Letts schoolgirl diaries. I kept them in my sock drawer, madly thinking this was an amazingly inventive hiding place. I didn't really record any riveting secrets in my blotchy biro: 'Mummy bought me a *Girl* comic. I think Joan of Arc is wonderful. Daddy and I went for a walk and I pretended to be a pony.'

I didn't write at length in a proper journal until I was in my teens. I read *The Diary of Anne Frank* and then re-read it so many times I could quote whole passages by heart. I especially loved the parts where Anne says she wants to be a writer when she grows up. I identified so strongly with that longing. I ached for Anne because she never had the chance to fulfil her huge potential. However, she also wrote that she wanted to be remembered after her death, and of course millions around the world read her wonderful diary. I knew this perfectly well but I still somehow felt she was writing her diary just for

1

me, confiding all her secret fears and hopes and dreams. I slept with my pink Pan paperback copy of Anne's diary under my pillow and I kept a picture of her on my bedside table. I'd sometimes whisper to her at night.

I'd seen a photo of the actual red and white checked notebook that was Anne's first diary. I longed to own a similar notebook. Stationery was pretty dire back in the late fifties and early sixties. There was no such thing as Paperchase. I walked round and round the stationery counter in Woolworths and spent most of my pocket money on notebooks, but they weren't strong on variety. You could have shiny red sixpenny notebooks, lined inside, with strange maths details about rods and poles and perches on the back. (I never found out what they were!) Then you could have shiny *blue* sixpenny notebooks, etc. That was your lot.

I was enchanted to read in Dodie Smith's novel *I Capture the Castle* that the heroine, Cassandra, was writing her diary in a similar sixpenny notebook. She eventually progressed to a shilling notebook. My Woolworths rarely stocked such expensive luxuries. Then, two thirds of the way through the book, Cassandra is given a two-guinea red leather manuscript book. I lusted after that fictional notebook for years.

2

I told my mother, Biddy. She rolled her eyes. It could have cost two *hundred* guineas – both were way out of our league.

'Could I maybe have a special journal for my Christmas present?' I begged.

'Can't you use one of the notepads Harry brings home from work?' she asked.

My dad, Harry, was a civil servant. One of the few perks of his job was that he had an unlimited illegal supply of notepads watermarked SO – Stationery Office. I'd drawn on these pads for years, I'd scribbled stories, I'd written letters. They were serviceable but unexciting: thin cream paper unreliably bound at the top with glue. You couldn't write a journal in one of these notepads; it would fall apart in days.

'I need proper covers for my secret journal. I want it to be completely private,' I said.

Biddy scoffed at me. She didn't believe in privacy, especially where I was concerned. But she was always inventive with my Christmas presents even though we had very little money. She rose to the journal challenge.

On Christmas Day 1959, when I was just fourteen, she gave me a book, *The Devil and Mary Ann* by Catherine Cookson (I'd read the first two books about this tough little Tyneside girl and loved them); a *Filmgoers' Annual* with a special feature on Dirk Bogarde; a pair of American tan nylons and my first white lace suspender belt; a Yardley pressed powder compact in a gilt case – *and a proper journal.*

It wasn't quite a red-leather two-guinea job. It was grey plastic and it didn't cost a penny. Biddy worked as a book-keeper for Prince Machines. They supplied some of these machine tools to Thailand. Their customers sent them a diary as a seasonal token. The lettering was all Thai and therefore meaningless to me, but it was easy enough to work out which page was 1 January.

I was thrilled with my diary. It was the size of a book so I had quite a lot of room to write in. Here's that first entry:

Ever since I was little I have loved writing stories and poems. I would get an idea, buy a new exercise book, and start writing industriously, thinking myself the creator of a masterpiece. But by the end of the week I would think of another better idea and repeat the rigmarole. But now I have the better idea of writing a diary, as I hope I will never get sick of my own life. Besides, think of all the people who have been made famous by their diaries. Samuel Pepys, Fanny Burney, Marjorie Fleming, Anne Frank, etc., etc., so why shouldn't I? I'm only very

*ordinary, admittedly, but interesting things do
sometimes happen to me. But perhaps the real
reason for me starting this diary is because I find
it 'irresistible, the pleasure of popping down my
thoughts from time to time on paper'.*

I was quoting Anne Frank of course. I said '*etc.,
etc.,*' one of my weird little writing tics, though I
didn't know any other diarists, so I shouldn't have
put even one etc., let alone two.

I wrote with a lovely old-fashioned mottled
fountain pen. My handwriting was much neater
then than it is nowadays. My spelling wasn't always
too hot. It still isn't. Thank goodness for the
spellcheck on my computer!

I had a list of new year's resolutions too. They
didn't vary from year to year. Two out of three of
them are pretty embarrassing.

Number one: Grow my hair.

When I was a baby I'd had fine, dark, straight
hair. Biddy wound the top wisp round her finger
so it stuck up in a fetching little wave. Sadly, my
hair stayed thin and straight and wispy. Biddy
continued to wave the top, forcing me to sleep
with wicked curling grips seemingly stuck
directly into my scalp. She had the rest cut very
short to try to keep it tidy. I hated my hairstyle,

though I liked going to Bentalls children's hairdresser's because you got to crouch on a special seat with a horse's head sticking out between your knees. You could stroke the horse's mane and tickle his ears while having your hair clipped. If you were very good and didn't make a fuss, the hairdresser (Pam or Maureen or Marilyn) would spin you round and round when she'd finished snipping.

Biddy was still dissatisfied with my wispy waif appearance. She wished I had Shirley Temple ringlets so she dragged me to her own hairdresser's and had them perm my hair. I had one perm after another throughout my childhood. I hated hated hated perms. I looked as if I'd been plugged into a light socket. I still had violent perms the first couple of years of secondary school and got royally teased about my frizzy hair. Girls on the bus would snigger at my precariously balanced school beret.

'Does your mother have to put your beret on with a battering ram?'

Oh, very funny. As I got older I argued more and utterly refused to have any more perms.

'I'm going to grow my hair long,' I said firmly.

'But it won't suit you, Jac. And it's too fine. It'll go all straggly.'

'I don't care,' I said.

6

It *did* go straggly in that awful in-between stage. It took such a long time to grow. I'd take hold of it a lock at a time and pull it sharply, or I'd sit hunched up with my neck tucked in just so that I could kid myself my hair was nearly shoulder-length.

It started to get horribly greasy too, much to my horror. In those long-ago days you only washed your hair once a week with Drene shampoo. *Anyone's* hair would look greasy. I'd attack my head with dry shampoo, a ghastly white powdery substance like chalk. It *looked* as if I'd been rubbing chalk through my hair after I'd applied it. I can't understand why I didn't wash my hair properly each day. There was some mumbo-jumbo that it made you lose your strength!

I'd wince every time I looked in the mirror and suddenly weaken. I'd have my hair cut and permed, instantly hate my new middle-aged hairstyle and vow to grow my hair all over again.

I didn't just want long hair. I wanted *fair* hair too, though I didn't dare contemplate peroxide. Biddy said Peroxide Blondes were as Common as Muck. I longed ludicrously for natural long blonde hair. There was a girl called Susan Wooldridge in my year at school. She had shiny straight fair hair, neatly plaited in two long braids tied with green satin ribbon to match our green and grey school

7

uniform. I'd stand behind Susan in assembly and stare enviously at her beautiful hair. Susan was a pretty pink-and-white complexioned girl with a perky personality. I didn't know her very well because we weren't in the same class but I longed to *be* her.

When I woke up in the morning I'd keep my eyes shut, clench my fists and *will* myself to change places with Susan. Sometimes I'd kid myself it was actually working. I'd feel as if I was wafting way above the clouds, diving down over the rooftops of New Malden and slipping into Susan's open window. But when I dared open my eyes I always found myself under my own ugly brown eiderdown, and the mirror in my bedroom reflected my own artificial curls.

My second resolution was equally embarrassing: Get a boyfriend.

I'd had boyfriends at my primary school – David and then Alan – but of course they weren't *real* boyfriends, though we held hands and occasionally gave each other film-star kisses. We didn't keep in touch when we all went on to secondary school. I went to Coombe, an all-girls school, so I obviously wasn't going to find a new boyfriend there.

I didn't truthfully *want* a boyfriend, but it was such a status symbol, especially at school. When we all gathered together in the first year (Year

8

Seven) it was the first question everyone asked. *Have you got a boyfriend?*

Very few of us had boyfriends the first and second years so we could relax and not bother about it too much, but by the third year (Year Nine) it was starting to become imperative.

I still didn't know *how* to get a boyfriend. There were lots of boys who lived in our flats – in fact I lived right next door to two teenage boys, Jeremy and Anthony, but I didn't *know* them. I just mumbled hello if I bumped into them on the balcony.

I was painfully aware that Biddy thought me very backward when it came to boys. I knew she'd had heaps of boyfriends when she was fourteen.

'Don't worry, you'll get a boyfriend soon, Jac,' she'd say. 'Just smile at the first boy you fancy and start chatting to him.'

'What should I *say*?'

'*I* don't know. The first thing that comes into your head.'

I had a head full of daydreams. I couldn't imagine telling any boy about my private imaginary games, all my made-up characters and stories-in-progress. I didn't even talk about them to my best friends, Chris and Carol. I certainly didn't talk about them to Biddy, who thought me weird enough already.

'I don't know how to talk to boys,' I said despairingly.

'If only you weren't so *shy*,' said Biddy. 'Still, you can't help that, you take after your father.'

I didn't ask Harry how to talk to boys. I didn't know how to talk to *him*. We could spend a whole day together in the flat without saying a word to each other. It was hard remembering that Harry had once been Biddy's boyfriend. They weren't boy and girl now – and they certainly weren't friends either.

My third and final new year resolution was more heartfelt and personal:

Write a book!

I'd *written* so-called books, heaps of them, but they were twenty-page hand-written efforts in my Woolworths notebooks. Most petered out halfway through. Some only progressed for a page or two. I didn't restrict myself to novels. I wrote a fifteen-page biography of the child actress Mandy Miller, embellished with photos and drawings. It was pretty similar to all the Jacqueline Wilson projects children show me nowadays.

I wrote the odd play too – odd being the operative word. I once wrote about the story of Moses from his sister Miriam's point of view. I tried poetry too, most of it abysmal. I tried to be versatile as a writer but at heart I've always been a novelist. I tried so hard with my stories but I knew that none of them were good enough to get published. I just hoped that *one* day I'd write something worth while.

I kept that 1960 diary all the way through to the summer, writing very detailed entries day after day. I'll be quoting from almost every page – and blushing frequently!

Jacqueline with her grandparents

2
My Family

We were a small family, just Biddy, Harry and me, cooped up in our claustrophobic council flat in Kingston. There were a lot of arguments. Biddy and me, Harry and me, Biddy and Harry against me – and, most frequently of all, Biddy and Harry arguing between themselves.

I rarely go into details of these arguments in my 1960 diary. I just write at the bottom of many pages: 'Mummy and Daddy had a row.' These rows could blow up over the silliest things. Harry might moan about the way Biddy tucked his socks into a tight ball, or Biddy might raise her eyebrows and sniff in a snobbish way if Harry said, *'Pardon?'*. These tiny irritations would be like a starter's gun. Suddenly they were *off* – and the row would escalate until they were both shouting at the tops of their voices.

'For God's sake, what will the neighbours think?' Biddy would hiss when Harry was in mid rant. Harry would bellow that he couldn't care less about the neighbours – or words to that effect.

The Grovers at number eleven and the Hines at

number thirteen must have sighed and turned up their televisions, muttering 'Those dreadful Aitkens' again.

Yet it wasn't *all* rows and ranting. Biddy and Harry couldn't stand each other, and like all teenagers I sometimes felt I couldn't stand them – but we could still have fun together. On Sunday mornings, if Harry was in a good mood, he'd get up and make us breakfast. We weren't healthy eaters then. My absolute favourite Sunday-treat breakfast was fried potatoes on buttered toast, followed by another piece of toast spread with thick white sugary condensed milk. My mouth is puckering as I write this. Nowadays I couldn't swallow so much as a teaspoon of ultra-sweet condensed milk to save my life, but when I was fourteen I could have slurped up a whole tin at a time.

We ate a large Sunday roast together too while listening to *The Billy Cotton Band Show* and *Family Favourites* on the radio. We particularly enjoyed listening to *Hancock's Half Hour* as a family, all three of us convulsing with laughter. We watched television together in the evenings. For a long time we only had one television channel so there weren't any arguments about which programme to pick.

There must have been many ordinary cosy evenings like this:

Thursday 3 March
I'm sitting at the table. The time is twenty to eight.
'Life of Bliss' is on the T.V. Daddy has just got in
from work. I ask Mummy what happened at her
office. Mr Lacy was in a good mood, she replies,
and goes back to her newspaper. What are you
looking for? Mummy asks Dad. My black pen, he
replies, have I got time for a bath before supper?
Only an in and out says Mummy. Daddy has his
bath. We sit down to our supper of macaroni cheese
(one of my favourites). After supper I do my maths
homework. Daddy helps, bless him. Then I watch
T.V. It is a Somerset Maugham play, and very good.
P.S. Mum bought me some sweet white nylon
knickers.

I was still very close to Biddy and struggled hard
to please her. I took immense pains to find an
original Mother's Day present for her. I went
shopping in Kingston with my friends Carol and
Cherry, all of us after Mother's Day presents –
though we got a little distracted first.

We first went to Maxwells the record shop, and I
bought the record 'A Theme from a Summer Place'.
It was lovely. Then we went to Bentalls. First we

went to the Yardley make-up, and a very helpful woman sold me my liquefying cleansing cream and Cherry a new lipstick. Then we bought our mothers some cards, and Cherry bought her mother some flowers, and Carol bought her mother some chocs. But I knew what I wanted for my adorable, queer, funny, contemporary mother. A pair of roll-on black panties, a pair of nylons and a good (expensive) black suspender belt.

I record happily on Sunday: '*Mum was very pleased with her panties, belt and nylons.*'

I tried to please Harry too. I didn't buy him a vest and Y-fronts for Father's Day, thank goodness – but I did make an effort.

Saturday 4 June
I bought a card for Father's Day, and some men's talcum and three men's hankies as well.

Biddy and Harry bought me presents too, sometimes vying with each other, to my advantage: '*Biddy gave me a pound to spend for when I'm going round Kingston with Carol – and then Harry gave me five pounds. For nothing!!!*'

They could be imaginative with gifts. Biddy not

only bought me all my clothes, she bought me books and ornaments and make-up. Harry tried hard too. He was away up in Edinburgh for a week on business (I wrote, 'It feels so strange in the flat without Daddy'), but when he came back he had bought lavish presents for both of us:

Saturday 21 May
Daddy came back from Scotland today. He gave me a little Scotch doll, a typewriter rubber, a coin bracelet, an expensive bambi brooch, and a little book about Mary, Queen of Scots. He gave Mummy a £5 note.

Harry could be generous with his time too. That summer of 1960 I had to do a Shakespeare project so he took a day off work and we went to Stratford. It was a *good* day too. We went round Shakespeare's birthplace and Anne Hathaway's cottage and collected various postcards and leaflets. My project was the most gorgeously illustrated of anyone's. But he mostly kept to himself, out at work on weekdays, still playing tennis at the weekends, and when he was at home he hunched in his armchair, surrounded by piles of *Racing Posts* and form books. If he wasn't going out he rarely bothered to

17

get dressed, comfortable in our centrally heated flat in pyjamas and dressing gown and bare feet.

Biddy frequently changed into her dressing gown too and sat watching television, tiny feet tucked up, her Du Maurier cigarettes on one arm of the chair and a bag of her favourite pear drops on the other. As the evening progressed, one or other of them would start nodding and soon they would both be softly snoring. I'd huddle up with my book, happy to be left in peace way past my bed time.

They never went out in the week but they started going out on Saturday nights with Biddy's friend Ron. They must have been strange evenings, especially as my parents were practically teetotal. Biddy stuck with her bitter lemons. Harry tried a pint of beer occasionally but hated it. One Saturday night he pushed the boat out and had two or three and came home feeling so ill he lay on the kitchen floor, moaning.

'Well, it's all your own fault, you fool. You were the one who poured the drink down your throat,' said Biddy, poking him with her foot.

Harry swore at her, still horizontal.

'Don't you start calling me names! Now get up, you look ridiculous. What if someone walks along the balcony and peers in the kitchen window? They'll think you're dead.'

'I wish I was,' said Harry, and shut his eyes.

18

I don't think he enjoyed those Saturday nights one iota – and yet he agreed to go on a summer holiday that year with Ron and his wife, Grace. I don't know if Harry had any particular secret lady friends at that time – he certainly did later on in his life. I think Biddy and Harry came very close to splitting up when I was fourteen or so. I know Ron had plans to go to Africa and wanted Biddy to go with him. But I was the fly in the ointment, flapping my wings stickily. Biddy wouldn't leave me, so *she* was stuck too.

We went out very occasionally on a Sunday afternoon, when we caught the bus to the other end of Kingston and went to tea with my grandparents, Ga and Gongon. The adults played solo and bridge and bickered listlessly and ate Cadbury's Dairy Milk chocolates. I ate chocolates too and curled up with my book. If I finished my own book I read one of Ga and Gongon's Sunday school prize books or flipped through their ten volumes of Arthur Mee's *Children's Encyclopedia*.

I preferred visiting Ga by myself. I'd go on Wednesday afternoons after school. She'd always have a special tea waiting for me: thinly sliced bread and butter and home-made loganberry jam, tinned peaches and Nestlé's tinned cream, and then a cake – a Peggy Brown lemon meringue tart if Ga had shopped in Surbiton, or a Hemming's Delight (meringue and artificial cream with a glacé cherry) if she had been to Kingston marketplace.

Ga would chat to me at tea, asking me all about school, taking me ultra seriously. I should have been the one making *her* tea as her arthritis was really bad now. She had to wear arm splints and wrist supports, and for a week or so before her monthly cortizone injection she could only walk slowly, clearly in great pain. It's so strange realizing that Ga then was younger than me now. She looked like an old lady in her shapeless jersey suits and black buttoned shoes.

One Wednesday it was pouring with rain and I was sodden by the time I'd walked to Ga's, my hair in rats' tails, my school uniform dripping. Ga gave me a towel for my hair and one of her peachy-pink rayon petticoats to wear while my clothes dried. But when it was time for me to go home they were still soaking wet. I didn't particularly mind but Ga wouldn't hear of me walking the three quarters of an hour home up Kingston Hill in sopping wet clothes. She was sure I'd catch a chill. She insisted I borrow one of her suits. She meant so well I couldn't refuse, though I absolutely died at the thought of walking home in old-lady beige with her long sagging skirt flapping round my ankle socks.

Ga could no longer make her own clothes because her hands had turned into painful little

20

claws due to her arthritis – but she would press her lips together firmly and *make* herself sew if it was for me.

Wednesday 27 January
After school went up to Ga's. She has made my Chinese costume for the play, and also gave me a lovely broderie anglaise petticoat. Isn't she kind?

Yes, she was *very* kind, in little sweet ways. On 14 February I always received a Valentine. That year it was two little blue birds kissing beaks, perching on two red hearts outlined with glitter. There were forget-me-nots and roses sprinkled across the card, and inside a little printed verse and an inked question mark. I knew it wasn't from a boy, although I was supposed to assume it came from a secret admirer. I was pretty certain it was Ga wanting to give me a surprise, sending me a Valentine so I could show it off at school.

She was always so reassuring and comforting.

Wednesday 24 February
Back to school, worst luck. Going to school all Wolverton Avenue was dug up and there were many

workmen standing around and digging under the pavement. Sue at once crossed the road, but I stayed on the left side where they were working and each time they smiled and said hello and how are you, etc. in the friendly way workmen do, I smiled back and said hello, and I feel fine. Afterwards Sue was ever so crabby and said in what I call her 'old maid' voice, 'I saw you smile at all those <u>work</u> men.' Talk about a bloody snob! She makes me MAD at times. I told Ga when I went up there this afternoon after school and she (the darling) said I had a nice little face and naturally they would smile and talk to me, and that it was only polite that I should do the same back.

Ga was so gentle with me, letting me rant on in a half-baked manner about becoming a pacifist and banning the bomb and being anti-apartheid, while she nodded and smiled. I got tremendously steamed up at the end of term because we were having a party for all the girls at school, with music and non-alcoholic punch.

'It's not *fair!*' I said.

'You can't have real punch at a school party,' she said reasonably.

'Oh no, I don't mind the non-alcoholic punch part. I don't *like* proper drink,' I said.

She looked relieved. 'So *what* isn't fair?' she asked.

'We can't have boys! Can you imagine it, just us girls dancing together all evening. That's not a proper party, it's just like dancing school. We're all furious, wanting to take our boyfriends.'

Ga blinked. 'So, have you got a boyfriend, Jac?'

'Well . . . no, I haven't, not at the moment. But that's not the point, it's the *principle* that matters,' I said, determined not to lose face.

Ga was kind enough not to laugh at me.

3
Clothes

Saturday 2 January
*I went to Bentalls' sale with Mum. We got some
smashing bargains so I'm jolly glad I went. First
a very full pink and mauve mohair skirt, and to go
with it a lovely pink thick-knit Austrian cardigan.
We got it for 45 bob, but previously it had been
£9.9s!! I also got a good book and a new lipstick. I
tried it out this afternoon and wore my new outfit,
and I think I looked quite nice. I looked warm, cosy
and fashionable, nice and teenager-y, but not
looking too grown up.*

I can't believe I once used words like *jolly* and
smashing! I sound like someone out of Enid
Blyton's Famous Five books. That pink and mauve
mohair skirt and Austrian cardigan sound
absolutely hideous too, though I obviously liked
them at the time. I didn't actually *want* to look
'nice and teenager-y'.

If you wanted to look truly cool in 1960 you
dressed like a Beatnik. You had long straight hair

(sigh!). You wore black: black polo-neck jumper, black skirt, black stockings, black pointy boots, with a black duffel coat over the top. You were probably roasting to death in all these woolly layers but you *looked* cool. I'd have given anything to be a Beatnik but it would have looked like fancy dress on a schoolgirl living on a suburban council estate. Beatniks were exotic adults who lived in London and haunted smoky jazz cellars.

The cool look at school was totally different. Girls backcombed their hair into bouffant styles and then sprayed it until it hardened into a helmet. They cinched in their waists with elasticated belts and stuck out their skirts with nylon petticoats. You could get wonderfully coloured petticoats at Kingston Monday market – pink, blue, even bright yellow, edged with lace. You washed these petticoats in sugar water, which made them stiff. Your skirts bounced as you walked, showing your layers of petticoat. You wobbled when you walked too, in stiletto heels.

I say 'you'. *I* didn't have bouffant hair, elasticated belts, flouncy petticoats or stiletto heels.

'You're not going out looking as Common as Muck,' said Biddy.

I rather wanted to look as Common as Muck, but I couldn't manage it, even behind Biddy's back. I didn't know *how* to tease my hair into that amazing bouffant shape. It was either too frizzy or too limp, depending on whether I'd just had another dreaded perm or not.

I didn't have enough of a waist to cinch, and my petticoats were limp white garments that clung to my legs. I didn't have proper stilettos. My first pair of heels were barely an inch high. They were called Louis heels, squat, stumpy little heels on a slip-on shoe. I was used to straps or laces and I had to walk with my feet stuck out like a ballet dancer to keep them on. They were pale green. 'Eau de nil,' said Biddy. She bought me a silly little clutch purse too, also in eau de nil. I had Biddy's pass-me-down cream swagger coat that year. It draped in an odd way and had weird wide sleeves. I didn't swagger in my coat, I slouched, walking with kipper feet in my silly shoes, clutching the purse.

'You look so ladylike in that outfit,' said Biddy, smiling approvingly.

Biddy wasn't alone in wanting her daughter to look ladylike. At school that spring of 1960 we had a visit from the Simplicity paper-pattern people. I'd never sewn a garment in my life apart from a school apron I'd laboured over in needlework, but I certainly knew my way around the Simplicity fashion books. I'd been buying them for years so that I could cut out all the most interesting models and play pretend games with

27

them. It was strange seeing familiar dresses made up, worn by real girls.

Thursday 17 March
We missed Latin today! The fashion people, Simplicity, had made up some of their teenage patterns and our girls dressed up in them, and we had a fashion parade. It was quite good, and our girls looked quite different, being all posh, and wearing white gloves, and walking like proper models. (Only they looked a bit daft.) I didn't mind the dresses, but I didn't see one I really liked. Afterwards the lady told us that we should wear bras to define and shape our figures (we already do wear them of course), that we should use deodorants (which I at any rate do), that we should pay attention to our deportment (which I try to do), that we should think carefully whether our lipsticks go with our dresses (which I do) etc., etc.

Heavens! I might go in for a spot of lipstick co-ordination but I certainly didn't want to wear ladylike *white gloves*. The very last thing in the world I wanted to look was *ladylike*. At least the pink of the mohair skirt wasn't pastel, and the skirt was full enough to bunch out as much as possible.

I could hide my lack of waist under the chunky cardigan. I expect the lipstick was pink too. Later on in the sixties make-up changed radically and I'd wear *white* lipstick and heavy black eye make-up, but in 1960, when I was fourteen, the 'natural' look was still in vogue.

I wasn't great at putting on make-up. I rubbed powder on my face, smeared lipstick on my lips, brushed black mascara on my lashes and hoped for the best. It didn't help that I wore glasses. I had to take them off when I applied my make-up and consequently couldn't quite see what I was doing.

I've looked through the photo album covering my teenage years and I can't find a single picture of me wearing my glasses. I hated wearing them. I'm not sure contact lenses were widely available in those days. I'd certainly never heard of them. I was stuck wearing my glasses in school. I couldn't read the blackboard without them. I could barely see the board itself. But *out* of school I kept them in the clutch bag.

I had to whip them on quick while waiting at a bus stop so I could stick my hand out for the right number bus, but the moment I was *on* the bus I'd shove the glasses back in the bag. I spent most of my teenage years walking round in a complete haze, unable to recognize anyone until they were nose to nose with me. I was clearly taking my life in my hands whenever I crossed the road. I was an accident waiting to happen, especially as I made up stories in my head as I walked along and didn't even try to concentrate on where I was going.

I was in the middle of an imaginary television interview one day going home from school.

'Do tell us what inspired you to write this wonderful novel, Miss Aitken,' the interviewer asked as I jumped off the bus.

He never got an answer. I stepped out into the road and walked straight into a car. I was knocked flying, landing with a smack on the tarmac. The interviewer vanished. *I* vanished too, losing consciousness. I opened my eyes a minute or two later to find a white-faced man down on his knees beside me, clutching my hand.

'Oh, thank God you're not dead!' he said, nearly in tears.

I blinked at him. It was almost like one of my own fantasies. When Biddy or Harry were especially impatient with me I'd frequently imagine myself at my last gasp on my deathbed, with them weeping over me, begging my forgiveness.

'I'm so sorry!' he said. 'It wasn't my *fault*, you just walked straight in front of me. I braked but I couldn't possibly avoid you. Where do you hurt?'

'I don't think I actually hurt anywhere,' I said, trying to sit up.

'No, you shouldn't move! I'd better find a phone box to call an ambulance.'

'Oh no, I'm fine, really,' I said, getting very worried now.

I *did* feel fine, though in a slightly dream-like, unreal way. I staggered to my feet and he rushed to help me.

'You really shouldn't stand!' he said, though I was upright now. 'Are your legs all right? And your arms?'

I shook all four of my limbs gingerly. One of my arms was throbbing now, *and* one of my legs, but I didn't want to upset him further by admitting this.

'Yes, they're perfectly OK,' I said. 'Well, thank you very much for looking after me. Goodbye.' I started to walk away but he looked appalled.

'I can't let you just walk off! The very least I can do is take you home to your mother. I want to explain to her what happened.'

'Oh no, really!'

'I insist!'

I dithered, nibbling my lip. I couldn't think clearly. Alarm bells were ringing in my head. Biddy had drummed it into me enough times: *Never get into a car with a strange man!* But he seemed such a nice kind strange man, and I was worried about hurting his feelings.

I tried to wriggle out of his suggestion tactfully.

'My mum isn't *at* home,' I said. 'So you won't be able to explain to her. *I'll* tell her when she gets home from work. I promise I'll explain it was all my fault.'

I went to pick up my satchel. I used the aching arm and nearly dropped it. I tried to hurry away, but the aching leg made me limp.

'You *are* hurt, I'm sure you are,' he said. 'Where does your mother work? I'm driving you there straight away, and then I'll drive you both to the hospital.'

I didn't have the strength for any more arguing. I let him help me into his car. Biddy's workplace, Prince Machines, was only five minutes' drive away. If he drove fast in the wrong direction, intent on abducting me, then I'd simply have to fling open the car door and hurl myself out. I'd survived one car accident, so hopefully I'd survive a second.

Yes, I know. I was mad. Don't anyone ever get in a car with a stranger under any circumstances whatsoever.

However, my stranger proved to be a perfect gentleman, parking the car in the driveway of Prince Machines, supporting me under the arm, carrying my satchel on his own back. Biddy looked out of the office window and saw us approaching.

She shot out of the office and came charging up

to us. 'Jac? What's happened? Who's this? Are you all right?'

'This is my mum,' I said unnecessarily.

The stranger explained, anxiously asserting again that it really wasn't his fault.

Biddy didn't doubt him. 'You're so *hopeless*, Jac! Haven't I told you to look where you're going? You were daydreaming, weren't you? When will you *learn*?'

I hung my head while Biddy ranted.

'Still, thank goodness you're all right,' she said finally, giving me a quick hug.

'Well, I'm not quite sure she *is* all right,' said my rescuer. 'I think she was unconscious for a minute or two. She seems pretty shaken up. I'm very happy to drive you to hospital.'

'Oh, for goodness' sake, she's fine. There's no need whatsoever,' said Biddy. 'Who wants to hang around the hospital for hours?'

Biddy had once worked there delivering newspapers to patients and had a healthy contempt for the place. She always swore she'd never set foot in the hospital even if she was dying.

She had more authority than me and sent the stranger on his way. He was kind enough to pop back the following day with the biggest box of chocolates I'd ever seen in my life. I'd never been given so much as a half-pound of Cadbury's Milk

Tray before. I lolled on my bed in my baby-doll pyjamas all weekend with my giant box beside me. I'd seen pictures of big-busted film starlets lounging on satin sheets eating chocolates. I pretended I was a film star too. I can't have looked very beguiling: I had one arm in a sling and one leg was black with bruises from my thigh down to my toes.

Biddy had had to drag me up to the dreaded hospital after all. My aching arm became so painful I couldn't pick anything up and my bad leg darkened dramatically. We spent endless hours waiting for someone to tell us that I'd sprained my arm badly and bruised my leg.

'As if that wasn't blooming obvious,' Biddy muttered.

At least it got me out of PE at school for the next couple of weeks, so I didn't have to change into the ghastly aertex shirt and green divided shorts.

I cared passionately about clothes, but most of the time I was stuck wearing my school uniform. The winter uniform wasn't too terrible: white shirts, green and yellow ties, plain grey skirts and grey V-necked sweaters. We had to wear hideous grey gabardine raincoats, and berets or bowler-type hats with green and yellow ribbon round the brim. Earnest girls wore the hats, cool girls wore berets.

We had to wear white or grey socks or pale stockings kept up with a suspender belt or a 'roll-on'. Oh dear, underwear was so not sexy in 1960! Those roll-ons were hilarious. They weren't as armour-plated as the pink corsets our grannies wore, but they were still pretty fearsome garments. You stepped into them and then yanked them up over your hips as best you could, wiggling and tugging and cursing. It was even more of a performance getting out of them at the end of the day. I'm sure that's why so many girls never went further than chastely kissing their boyfriends. You'd die rather than struggle out of your roll-on in front of anyone. They had two suspenders on either side to keep up your stockings. Nylons took a sizeable chunk of pocket money so we mostly wore old laddered ones to school. We stopped the ladders running with dabs of pink nail varnish, so everyone looked as if they had measles on their legs.

We had to wear clunky brown Clarks shoes – an outdoor and an indoor pair – though some of the older girls wore heels on the way home if they were meeting up with their boyfriends. They customized their uniforms too, hitching up their skirts and pulling them in at the waist with those ubiquitous elasticated belts. They unbuttoned the tops of their blouses and loosened their ties and folded their berets in half and attached them with kirby grips to the back of their bouffant hair. We were younger and meeker and nerdier in my year and mostly wore our uniform as the head teacher intended.

Everyone cordially hated the summer uniform: canary-yellow dresses in an unpleasant synthetic material. There is not a girl in existence who looks good in canary yellow. It makes pale girls look sallow and ill, and rosy-cheeked girls alarmingly scarlet. The dresses had ugly cap sleeves, like silly wings, unflattering to any kind of arm and embarrassing when you put up your hand in class.

Very few people had washing machines in those days. You did your main wash once a week, so by Friday our canaries were stained and dingy. We had to wear straw boaters going to and from school even if there was a heatwave. These were hard, uncomfortable hats that made your head itch. They could only be kept in place with elastic. Nasty boys would run past and tip our boaters so that the elastic snapped under our chins. *Particularly* nasty boys would snatch at our backs to twang our bra elastic too. I often wonder *why* I wanted a boyfriend!

I looked younger than my age in my school uniform, but I did my best to dress older outside school – sometimes for particular reasons!

Thursday 4 February
After school I went to the pictures with Sue and
Cherry. I wore my red beret, black and white coat
and black patent shoes and managed to get in for
16 as the picture was an 'A'.

I sound too twee for words. A beret? But at least
it was a change from eau de nil. Green still figured
prominently in my wardrobe though.

Saturday 12 March
In the afternoon I went shopping with Mummy and
we bought me a pale green checked woolly
shirtwaister for the Spring to go with my green
shoes and handbag.

Just call this the lettuce look. However, I seemed
to like it then. In May I wrote:

After dinner I got dressed in my new green
shirtwaister, that I think suits me very well. Then,
loaded down with records, I called for Sue and we
went to Cherry's party. Everyone had brought lots
of records, and did my feet ache after all that jiving!

Carol wore her new black and white dress which looked nice.

My writing was certainly as limp as a lettuce in those days. *Nice!*

So I liked my green dress, but my favourite outfit was 'a cotton skirt patterned with violets and nice and full'. It's about the only one of those long-ago garments I wouldn't mind wearing now on a summer day.

Biddy was generous to me, buying me clothes out of her small wage packet.

Saturday 4 June
In the afternoon Mummy and I went to Richmond and after a long hunt we bought me a pair of cream flatties, very soft and comfortable. Then, back in Kingston, we went into C & A's and found a dress in the children's department that we both liked very much. The only trouble with it was that it had a button missing at the waist. Mummy made a fuss about it, but they didn't have another dress in stock or another button, so we bought it minus the button as we liked it very much indeed. It is a lovely powder blue colour with a straight skirt and Mummy

has transferred the bottom button to the waist so that it doesn't notice so much.

I sound like little Goody-Two-Shoes, trotting round with Mummy, being ever so grateful for my girly frock. It's reassuring to see that I revert to surly teenager the very next day.

Sunday 5 June
I AM A PIG. I was rude and irritable today and I just didn't care, and I spoilt Mummy's day at the coast. (Daddy wasn't very well-behaved either though!) I won't write any more about a very unfortunate day.

I wish I had. It would have been a lot more interesting than painstaking accounts of buttons missing on powder-blue dresses!

4
Chris

Sunday 3 January
Chris and Carol are my best friends, and there is
also Sue who lives next door, and Cherry down the
road. They all go to Coombe, my school.

I met my very special friend, Chris, on my first
day at Coombe County Secondary School for Girls.
I'd had *another* Christine as my special friend when
I was at primary school but we'd sadly lost touch
when we both left Latchmere. I think she moved
away after her mum died.

I'd never set eyes on my new friend Chris
before that first day at secondary school. I
didn't know anyone at all. It's always a bit scary
going to a brand-new school. Coombe was in New
Malden, two or three miles from our flats in
Kingston. I hadn't made it through my eleven plus
to Tiffin Girls' School, but I'd been given a 'second
chance' and managed to pass this time. I could
now go to a new comprehensive school instead of
a secondary modern.

41

Coombe was one of the first comprehensives, though it was divided firmly into two teaching streams – grammar and secondary modern. In an effort to make us girls mix in together, we were in forms for non-academic lessons like singing and PE, and in groups graded from one all the way to nine for lessons like maths and English. This system didn't make allowances for girls like me. I'd been put in group one, where I held my own in English and most of the arts subjects – but I definitely belonged in group nine for maths! Still, compiling that timetable must have been nightmare enough without trying to accommodate weird girls like me – very good in some subjects and an utter dunce in others.

I couldn't even get my head around the densely printed timetable, and the entire geography of the school was confusing. We weren't shown around beforehand or even given a map when we arrived the first day. We were somehow expected to *sense* our way around.

I managed to fetch up in the right form room, 1A. We stood around shyly, eyeing each other up and down. We were a totally mixed bunch. A few of the girls were very posh, from arty left-wing families who were determined to give their daughters a state education. Some of the girls were very tough, from families who didn't give their daughters' education a second thought. Most of us were somewhere in the middle, ordinary suburban girls fidgeting anxiously in our stiff new uniforms, wondering if we'd ever make friends.

'Good morning, Form One A! I'm Miss Crowford, your form teacher.'

'Good-morning-Miss-Crowford,' we mumbled.

She was small and dark and quite pretty, so we could have done a lot worse. I hoped she might teach English, but it turned out she was the gym teacher. I started to go off her immediately, though she was actually very kind and did her best to encourage me when I couldn't climb the ropes and thumped straight *into* rather than over the wooden horse.

Miss Crowford let us choose our own desks. I sat behind a smallish girl with long light-brown hair neatly tied in two plaits. We all had to say our names, going round the class. The girl with plaits said she was called Christine. I was predisposed to *like* girls called Christine so I started to take proper notice of her.

Miss Crowford was busy doing the Jolly-Teacher Talk about us being big girls now in this lovely new secondary school. She told us all about the school badge and the school motto and the school hymn while I inked a line of small girls in school uniform all round the border of my new and incomprehensible timetable.

Then a loud electronic bell rang, startling us. We were all used to the ordinary hand-bells rung at our primary schools.

'Right, girls, join your groups and go off to your next lesson,' said Miss Crowford. 'Don't dawdle! We only give you five minutes to get to the next classroom.'

I peered at my timetable in panic. It seemed to indicate that group one had art. I didn't have a clue where this would be. All the other girls were getting up purposefully and filing out of the room. In desperation I tapped Christine on the back.

'Excuse me, do you know the way to the art room?' I asked timidly.

Chris smiled at me. 'No, but I've got to go there too,' she said.

'Let's go and find it together,' I said.

It took us much longer than five minutes. It turned out that the art room wasn't even in the main school building, it was right at the end of the playground. By the time we got there I'd made a brand-new best friend.

Coombe had only been open for two years, so there weren't that many girls attending, just us new first years, then the second and third years. We barely filled half the hall when we filed into assembly. It was a beautiful hall, with a polished parquet floor. No girl was allowed to set foot on it in her outdoor shoes. We had to have hideous rubber-soled sandals so that we wouldn't scratch the shiny floorboards. We also had to have black plimsolls for PE. Some of the poorer girls tried to make do with plimsolls for their indoor shoes. Miss Haslett, the head teacher, immediately protested, calling the offending girls out to the front of the hall.

'They are *plimsolls*,' she said. 'You will wear proper indoor shoes tomorrow!'

I couldn't see what possible harm it would do letting these girls wear their plimsolls. Why were they being publicly humiliated in front of everyone? It wasn't their fault they didn't possess childish Clarks sandals. None of us earned any money. We couldn't buy our own footwear. It was a big struggle for a lot of families to find three pairs of shoes for each daughter – *four* pairs, because most girls wouldn't be seen dead in Clarks clodhoppers outside school.

However, the next day all the girls were wearing regulation sandals apart from one girl, Doreen, in my form. She was a tiny white-faced girl with bright red hair. She might have been small but she was so fierce we were all frightened of her. Doreen herself didn't seem frightened of anyone, not even Miss Haslett.

Doreen danced into school the next day, eyes bright, chin up. She didn't flinch when Miss Haslett called her up on the stage in front of everyone. None of Doreen's uniform technically passed muster. Her scrappy grey skirt was home-made and her V-neck jumper hand-knitted. She wore droopy white socks – and her black plimsolls.

Miss Haslett pointed at them in disgust, as if they were covered in dog's muck. 'You are still wearing plimsolls, Doreen! Tomorrow you will come to school wearing *indoor shoes*, do you hear me?'

Doreen couldn't help hearing her, she was bellowing in her face. But she didn't flinch.

We all wondered what would happen tomorrow. We knew Doreen didn't *have* any indoor shoes, and she didn't come from the sort of family where her mum could brandish a full purse and say, 'No problem, sweetheart, we'll trot down to Clarks shoeshop and buy you a pair.'

Doreen walked into school assembly the next morning in grubby blue bedroom slippers with holes in the toes. I'm certain this was all she had. She didn't look as if she was being deliberately defiant. There was a flush of pink across her pale face. She didn't want to show off the state of her slippers to all of us. Miss Haslett didn't understand. She flushed too.

46

'How *dare* you be so insolent as to wear your slippers in school!' she shrieked. 'Go and stand outside my study in disgrace.'

Doreen stood there all day long, shuffling from one slippered foot to the other. She didn't come into school the next day. The following Monday she wore regulation rubber-soled school sandals. They were old and scuffed and had obviously belonged to somebody else. Maybe someone gave them to her, or maybe her mum bought them for sixpence at a jumble sale.

'At last you've seen sense, Doreen,' said Miss Haslett in assembly. 'I hope this has taught you all a lesson, girls.'

I hadn't seen sense. I'd seen crass stupidity and insensitivity on Miss Haslett's part. It taught me the lesson that some teachers were appallingly unfair, so caught up in petty rules and regulations that they lost all compassion and common sense.

A couple of years later *I* ended up standing in disgrace outside Miss Haslett's study door. She'd seen me walking to the bus stop without my school beret and – shock horror! – I was sucking a Sherbet Fountain. I'd committed not one but two criminal offences in her eyes: eating in school uniform and not wearing my silly hat.

Miss Haslett sent for me and started telling me

off. 'Why were you eating that childish rubbish, Jacqueline?' she asked.

The obvious answer was that I was hungry, and I needed something to keep me going for the long walk home. (I'd stopped taking the bus after the dramatic accident.) However, I sensed Miss Haslett would consider an honest answer insolent, so I kept quiet.

'And *why* weren't you wearing your school beret?' she continued.

This was easier. 'I've lost it, Miss Haslett,' I said truthfully.

It had been there on my coat hook that morning. Someone had obviously snatched it for themselves when their own beret had gone missing.

'That's just like you, Jacqueline Aitken,' said Miss Haslett. 'Stand outside!'

I stood there. My legs started aching after a while so I leaned against the wall. I didn't feel cast down. I was utterly jubilant because I was missing a maths lesson. I gazed into space and started imagining inside my head, continuing a serial – a magic island story. Pupils squeaked past in their sandals every now and then, good girls trusted to take important messages to Miss Haslett. The odd teacher strode past too, several frowning at me to emphasize my disgrace. But then dear Mr Jeziewski, one of the art teachers, came sloping along in his suede shoes. He raised his eyebrows at me in mock horror, felt in his pocket, put two squares of chocolate on the window ledge beside me and winked before he went on his way.

I smiled at Mr Jeziewski and savoured my chocolate. I couldn't resist writing a similar scene in my book *Love Lessons*, in which my main girl, Prue, falls passionately in love with her art teacher, Mr Raxbury. I promise I *didn't* fall for Mr Jeziewski, who was very much a family man and rather plain, with straight floppy hair and baggy cords – but he was certainly my favourite teacher when I was at Coombe.

Having Chris for a friend was an enormous help in settling into secondary school life. She wasn't quite as hopeless as me at PE, but pretty nearly, so we puffed along the sports track together and lurked at the very edge of the playing field, pretending to be deep fielders.

We managed to sit next to each other in maths lessons so they were almost enjoyable. We didn't *learn* anything, though our teacher, Miss Rashbrook, was very sweet and gentle and did her best to explain – over and over again. I could have put poor Miss Rashbrook on a loop and played her explanation twenty-four hours a day, it would have made no difference whatsoever.

Chris and I pushed our desks close and tried to do our working out together – but mostly we chatted. We daydreamed about the future. We decided we'd stay friends for ever. We even wanted to live next door to each other after we got married. We could see the row of neat suburban houses outside the window and picked out two that were ours. (I had private dreams of a more Bohemian adult life, living romantically in a London garret with an artist – but wondered if I could do that at the weekends and settle down in suburbia Monday to Friday.)

We don't live next door to each other now but we *did* stay great friends all through school and went on to technical college together. We used to go dancing and I was there the evening Chris met her future husband, Bruce. I was there at Chris's wedding; I was there – in floods of tears – at Bruce's funeral. We've always written and phoned and remembered each other's birthdays. We've been on several hilarious holidays, giggling together as if we were still schoolgirls.

Chris lived in New Malden so she went home for dinner, and at the end of school she walked one way, I walked the other, but the rest of the time we were inseparable. Chris soon asked me home to tea and this became a regular habit.

I *loved* going to Chris's house. She had a

storybook family. Her dad, Fred Keeping, was a plumber, a jolly little man who called me Buttercup. He had a budgie that perched on his shoulder and got fed titbits at meal times. Chris's mum, Hetty, was a good cook: she made Victoria sponges and jam tarts and old-fashioned latticed apple pies. We always had a healthy first course of salad, with home-grown tomatoes and cucumber and a little bit of cheese and crisps. I had to fight not to be greedy at the Keepings. I could have gone on helping myself to extra treats for hours. Chris's sister, Jan, was several years older and very clever but she chatted to me as if she was my friend too. We were all passionate about colouring. Chris and Jan shared a magnificent sharpened set of Derwent coloured pencils in seventy-two shades.

After Mrs Keeping had cleared the tea things and taken the embroidered tablecloth off the green chenille day cloth, we three girls sat up at the table and coloured contentedly. We all had historical-costume colouring books. Jan had the Elizabethans and coloured in every jewel and gem on Queen Elizabeth's attire exquisitely. Then she settled down to all her schoolwork while Chris and I went up stairs. We were supposed to be doing *our* homework up in Chris's bedroom, but we muddled through it as quickly as possible.

We did some mad projects together. For the first

two years at Coombe we did a combined history and geography lesson called 'social studies'. We learned all about prehistoric times, and made a plasticine and lolly-stick model of an early stilt village. We also started to write a long poem about a caveman family. We thought up our first line – *Many millions of years ago* – but then got stuck. We couldn't think of a rhyme for *ago*, so Chris looked up the word in Jan's rhyming dictionary. We ended up with:

> *Many millions of years ago*
> *Lived a woman who was a virago.*

perhaps the worst rhyme in many millions of years.

Mostly we simply played games like Chinese Chequers, Can You Go?, and Beetle, and made useless items with Scoubidou.

I loved Chris's bedroom, though it was very small and she didn't have anywhere near as many books as me. She had a little stable of china horse ornaments, big and small, because she longed passionately to go horse-riding, and saved up all her pocket money and birthday money for lessons. Her only other ornaments were plaster-cast Disney replicas of Snow White and the Seven Dwarfs. A few childhood teddies drooped limply on a chair, balding and button-eyed. Her clothes were mostly more childish than mine, though I hankered after her kingfisher-blue coat, a colour Biddy labelled vulgar – goodness knows why.

Chris's bedroom felt *safe*. You could curl up under her pink candlewick bedspread, read an old Blyton mystery book, and feel at peace. You wouldn't fall asleep and dream of mad men walking out of your wardrobe or monsters wriggling up from under your bed. You wouldn't wake to the sound of angry voices, shouts and sobbing. You would sleep until the old Noddy alarm clock rang and you could totter along to the bathroom in your winceyette pyjamas, the cat rubbing itself against your legs.

I'd slept at Chris's house several times, I'd been to lunch with her, I'd been to tea, I'd been on outings in their family car to Eastbourne, I'd been to Chris's birthday party, a cosy all-girls affair where we played old-fashioned games like Squeak Piggy Squeak and Murder in the Dark.

It was way past time to invite Chris back to my flat at Cumberland House. So Chris came one day after school and met Biddy and Harry. My home was so different from hers. Chris was very kind and a naturally polite girl. She said 'Thank you for having me' with seeming enthusiasm when she went home. I wonder what she *really* thought.

Maybe she liked it that there was no one in our flat to welcome us after school. It was fun having the freedom of the whole place, great to snack on as many chocolate biscuits as we wanted. When Biddy came home from work she cooked our tea: bacon and sausage and lots of chips, and served a whole plate of cakes for our pudding – sugary jam doughnuts, cream éclairs, meringues. Biddy considered this special-treat food and Chris nibbled her cakes appreciatively – but all that fatty food was much too rich for her sensitive stomach. She had to dash to the lavatory afterwards and was sick as discreetly as possible, so as not to offend Biddy. When Harry came home from work he was in a mood. He didn't call Chris Buttercup, he didn't say anything at all to her, just hid himself behind the *Sporting Life*.

Chris came on a sleepover once, and thank goodness everything went well. It was just like having a sister: getting ready for bed together and then whispering and giggling long into the night. We weren't woken by any rows, we slept peacefully cuddled up until the morning.'

However, Biddy and Harry couldn't always put on an amicable act. I remember when we got our first car, a second-hand white Ford Anglia. Biddy learned to drive and, surprisingly, passed her test before Harry. We decided to go on a trip to Brighton in our new car, and as a very special treat Chris was invited along too.

We sat in the back. I was dosed up with Quells, strong travel pills, so that I wouldn't be sick. They made me feel very dozy, but there was no danger of nodding off on *this* journey. Biddy and Harry were both tense about the outing and sniped at each other right from the start.

'Watch that lorry! For Christ's sake, do you want to get us all killed?' Harry hissed.

'Don't you use that tone of voice to me! And it was *his* fault, he was in the wrong ruddy lane,' said Biddy, her knuckles white on the steering wheel.

'*You're* in the wrong lane, you silly cow, if we're going to turn off at the Drift Bridge.'

'Who's driving this car, you or me? Ah, *I'm* driving because I'm the one who's passed the test!'

They chuntered on while I sat in the back with Chris, my tummy churning. I talked frantically, nattering about school and homework to try to distract her from my angry parents. I madly hoped she wouldn't even hear what they were saying. She talked back to me, valiantly keeping up the pretence, though she was very pale under her freckles.

Biddy and Harry had gone past the stage of being aware of us. We were stuck in a traffic jam going up Reigate Hill. The car started to overheat, as if reacting to its passengers. Biddy had to pull over and open the bonnet so the engine could cool down.

'It's your fault, you're driving like a maniac. You do realize you're ruining the car!' Harry said.

'If you don't like the way I drive, then *you* blooming well have a go,' said Biddy, bursting into tears.

'Oh yes, turn on the waterworks,' said Harry.

'Just shut up, will you? I'm sick of this,' Biddy sobbed. She opened her door and stumbled into the road. She ran off while we stared.

'That's so typical! Well, *I* can't ruddy well drive, as she's all too well aware,' said Harry – and *he* got out of the car, slammed the door with all his strength, and marched off in the opposite direction.

Chris and I sat petrified in the back of the car, our mouths open. Cars kept hooting as they swerved around us. I reached out for Chris's hand and she squeezed mine tight.

'You won't tell anyone at school?' I whispered.

'No, I promise,' she said. She paused. 'Jac, what if . . . what if they don't come back?'

I was wondering that myself. I couldn't drive, Chris couldn't drive. How would we ever get home? I thought about jumping out and flagging down a passing car to give us a lift. But they'd all be total strangers, it was far too dangerous. It was also obviously dangerous to be sitting in the back of a car parked at a precarious angle halfway up a hill heaving with traffic.

'They *will* come back,' I said firmly, trying to make myself believe it as well as Chris. I made my voice sound worldly wise and reassuring. 'They just need a few minutes to calm down.'

I was wondrously right. As I spoke I saw Biddy tottering back up the hill – and Harry appeared on the horizon too, strolling down towards us with his hands in his pockets. They both got back into the car as casually as if they'd just nipped out to spend a penny in the public toilets.

Biddy started up the car and we went up and over the hill, off to Brighton. Biddy and Harry barely spoke for the rest of the journey.

We had chicken and bread sauce for our lunch in a café near the beach, and then Chris and I were allowed to go off together. Biddy and Harry both gave us money. We scrunched up and down the pebbly beach, walked to the end of the pier and back, went all round the ornate pavilion, and treated ourselves to Mars bars and Spangles, two Wall's vanilla ice creams, and two portions of chips with salt and vinegar.

Heaven help us if Biddy and Harry had had another big row on the journey back. We'd have both been violently sick.

Jacqueline and Carol,
14-year-old schoolgirls

Jacqueline and Carol,
14-year-old young ladies

5
Carol

Girls' friendships are often complex. Chris was my best friend – but Carol was too. She lived in Kingston so we went home from school together, and we spent a lot of time in the holidays with each other. Both our mothers worked full-time so Carol and I spent day after day together.

I can't clearly remember going to Carol's house. I hardly knew her family. I met her mother but I can't remember her father. Carol had an older sister, Margaret, but she wasn't chatty and cosy like Jan, Chris's sister. I don't think she ever even spoke to me. Margaret looked years older than her age. She wore lots of make-up and high stiletto heels and had many boyfriends.

Carol seemed to be heading that way too. She was a dark, curvy girl with very white skin and full lips. By the time we were fourteen she could easily pass for seventeen or eighteen. She effortlessly managed all those teenage female things that I found a bit of a struggle: she plucked her eyebrows into an ironic arch, she shaved her legs smooth, she styled her hair and tied a silk scarf round it just like a film star. She was as expert as her sister with make-up, outlining her eyes and exaggerating her mouth into a moody coral pout.

Carol could be moody, full stop. I went round with her for several years but I never felt entirely at ease with her. We'd share all sorts of secrets but I always felt she was privately laughing at me, thinking me too earnest, too intense, and much too childish. Carol had two other friends, Linda and Margaret, sophisticated girls who flicked through the beauty pages of women's magazines in the lunch hour and yawned languidly because they'd been out late the night before with their boyfriends. I'd sit with the three of them each lunch time and feel utterly out of things. I'd risk a comment every now and then and catch Carol raising her immaculate eyebrows at Linda and Margaret.

She never openly criticized me, but sometimes it was the things she *didn't* say that hurt the most. I remember one time in the holidays I'd been maddened by my wispy hair straggling out of its annual perm. I'd taken myself off to a hairdresser's and asked for it to be cut really short. A few avant-garde girls were sporting urchin cuts that year and I thought they looked beautiful.

The trouble was, *I* wasn't beautiful. I was

appalled when I saw my terrible new haircut. It cruelly emphasized my glasses and my sticky-out ears. I went home and howled.

I was meeting Carol that afternoon. I felt so awful walking up to her and seeing her expression. I badly wanted her to say, 'Oh, Jacky, I love your new haircut, it really suits you.' We'd both know she was lying but it would be so comforting all the same.

Carol didn't say a word about my hair – but every now and then I caught her staring at me and shaking her head pityingly.

However, we did sometimes have great fun together. We both loved to go shopping, though neither of us had much pocket money. Kingston has always been a good town for shopping, though in 1960 Bentalls was just a big department store, not a vast shopping centre. We wandered round the make-up and clothes but we never actually bought anything there.

We had two favourite haunts, Woolworths and Maxwells. When I was fourteen, Woolworths was considered cool, a place where teenagers hung out. There was no New Look or Claire's Accessories or Paperchase or Primark or TopShop. I spent my pocket money in Woolworths. I walked straight past the toy counter now (though when Carol wasn't watching I glanced back wistfully at the little pink penny dolls) but I circled the stationery counter for hours.

It was there that I bought the red and blue sixpenny exercise books, or big fat shilling books if I was really serious about a story idea. I was forever buying pens too – red biro, blue biro, black biro, occasionally green – that was as varied as it got. There were no rollerballs, no gel pens, no felt tips. There were fountain pens but they didn't have cartridges then, so you needed a bottle of royal-blue Quink, and I always ended up with ink all over my fingers. I used to think that if I could only find the perfect notebook, the most stylish pen, my words would flow magically.

There's a little childish bit of me that still thinks that. I've got more ambitious in my taste. I thumb through beautiful Italian marbled notebooks now, trying to choose between subtle swirling blues and purples, pretty pale pinks and blues, bold scarlet with crimson leather spines and corners, wondering which is the luckiest, the one that will help me write a truly special story. I've bought a handful of expensive fountain pens, but I *still* end up with ink all over me so I generally stick to black miniballs.

I liked Woolworths jewellery too, big green or red or blue glass rings, 'emeralds' and 'rubies' and 'sapphires', for sixpence, and I loved the Indian glass bangles, treating myself to three at a time: pink and purple and blue. Biddy said it was common wearing so much jewellery at once. We'd both have been astonished to see me now, huge silver rings on every finger and bangles up to my elbows!

Monday 4 January
Met Carol in Kingston this morning. (We are still on holiday, go back to school next Wed. worst luck.) I bought a new pen from good old Woolworths, a pair of red mules, and some tomatoes for my lunch.

Woolworths sold old-lady slippers, cosy tartan with pompoms on the top, but of course I didn't want a pair of these. They were definitely grandma territory, and much as I loved Ga, I didn't want to look like her. No, these were special Chinese scarlet satin embroidered mules, incredibly exotic for those days. I was particularly keen on anything Chinese since reading a highly unsuitable adult book called *The World of Suzie Wong* by Richard Mason. Biddy might fuss excessively about the way I looked but she didn't always manage to monitor my reading matter.

Suzie Wong was a Chinese prostitute living in a

house of ill repute in Hong Kong. I thought her incredibly glamorous. I didn't necessarily want to copy her career choice, but I wished I *looked* like Suzie Wong: long straight glossy hair, and wearing a silk embroidered cheongsam split to the thighs. Both were way beyond my reach, but I *could* sport Chinese slippers from Woolworths. Well, I *couldn't* wear them actually. They were flat mules and I had the greatest difficulty keeping them on my feet. I walked straight-legged, toes clenched, but could only manage a couple of steps before walking straight out of them. I didn't care. I could simply sit with my legs stuck out and *admire* them.

We never went shopping in Kingston without going into Maxwells. It sold records. There weren't any HMV shops selling CDs in those days, let alone songs to buy on iTunes. Singles came on little '45' records in paper sleeves. They were actually doubles rather than singles, because each record had an A side (the potential chart topper), and then you flipped it over to the B side. You listened to the top twenty records in the hit parade on your little portable radio – only I didn't have one till I was fifteen, and I couldn't tune our big old-fashioned Home Service wireless to trendy Radio Luxembourg. I simply had to go to Maxwells with Carol and listen there. You told the spotty guy behind the desk that you wanted to listen to several records – Carol would reel off three or four likely titles – and then he would give them to you to take into the special listening booth.

We'd squash in together and then, when we started playing the records, we'd bob up and down in an approximation of dancing and click our fingers in time to the music. We considered ourselves very hip.

Sometimes there were other girls in the next listening booth. Sometimes there were boys, and then we'd bob and click a little more and toss our heads about. Sometimes there were older men, often comic stereotype leery old men in dirty raincoats. They'd peer through the window at us, their breath blurring the glass. We'd raise our eyebrows and turn our backs, not too worried because we were together.

We rarely *bought* a record. We played them several times and then slipped them back into their sleeves and returned them to the spotty boy.

'Sorry, we can't quite make up our minds,' we'd chorus, and saunter out.

Up until January 1960 I didn't even have a record player so it would have been a pointless purchase anyway. We had my grandparents' gramophone, one of those old-fashioned wind-up machines with a horn, but it wouldn't play modern

45 records. We had a pile of fragile 78s, that shattered if you dropped them, and I had my childhood Mandy Miller records, 'The Teddy Bears' Picnic', 'Doing the Lambeth Walk', and some Victor Silvester dance music. They weren't really worth the effort of strenuous handle-winding. But on 9 January everything changed.

I did the shopping with Dad and you'll never guess what we bought! A RECORD PLAYER! It had previously been £28 but had been marked down to £16. It is an automatic kind and plays beautifully. We bought 'Travelling Light' by Cliff Richard and Dad chose a Mantovani long player. It sounds very square but actually it is quite good with some nice tunes like 'Tammy', 'Que Sera Sera', 'Around the World in 80 Days'. I've been playing them, and all our old 78 records, all the afternoon.

I know, I know – Cliff Richard! But this wasn't the elderly Christian Cliff, this was when he was young and wild, with sideburns and tousled hair, wearing white teddy-boy jackets and tight black drainpipe trousers, very much an English Elvis, though he was never really as raunchy as Presley. I remember Celia, a lovely gentle girl in my class who was very into pop music. Her mother was too, surprisingly.

'My mum says she'd like to put Cliff to bed and tuck him up tight and give him a goodnight kiss – and she'd like to put Elvis to bed and get in beside him!' said Celia, chuckling.

Celia knew the words to every single pop song and would sometimes obligingly write them out for me in her beautiful neat handwriting. I would solemnly learn every single *bam-a-wham-bam* and *doobie-doobie-do* and also try hard to copy Celia's stylish script. There are passages in my diary where I'm trying out different styles, and it's clear when I'm doing my best to copy Celia.

I saved up my pocket money to buy another record the very next week: Michael Holliday's 'Starry Eyed'. It was currently Carol's favourite song and so we could do a duet together, though neither of us could sing to save our lives.

I didn't buy another record until March, when I decided on the theme tune from *A Summer Place*, a very sugary recording, all swirly violins, but I declared it 'lovely'. I had no musical taste whatsoever at fourteen. I'm astonished to see I next bought a Max Bygraves record, 'Fings Ain't Wot They Used t'Be'. I can hardly bear to write those words on the page!

By August I was staying up late on Saturday nights listening to David Jacobs's *Pick of the Pops*, and hearing 'Tell Laura I Love Her' by Ricky Valance for the first time. I *adored* 'Tell Laura'. It was like a modern ballad poem, a tragic sentimental song about a boy called Tommy trying to win a stockcar race in order to buy his girl a diamond ring. Each verse had a chorus of *'Tell Laura I love her'* – and of course Tommy's dying words from his wrecked car were *'Tell Laura I love her'*. I didn't take the song *seriously* but loved singing it over and over again in a lugubrious voice until Biddy screamed at me to stop that stupid row *now*.

Thank goodness my taste developed a little over the next year – in the summer of 1961 I discovered traditional jazz. I fell in love with all the members of the Temperance Seven, a stylish crowd of ex-art students who dressed in Edwardian costume. 'Whispering' Paul McDowell sang through a horn to make an authentic tinny sound. It was the sort of music my grandparents must once have played on their wind-up gramophone, but it seemed mint-new and marvellous to me: 'I bought Pasadena, it's an absolutely fab record and I've now played it at least 50 times.'

I went to see the Temperance Seven at Surbiton Assembly Rooms, and when I was sixteen I used to go up to London to various jazz cafés in Soho with a boyfriend. That was way in the future though. I might manage to just about *pass* for sixteen when I wanted to get into an A film at the cinema – but I certainly didn't act it.

Jacqueline with film star Jack Hawkins

TROY DONAHUE

AUDREY HEPBURN

CLIFF RICHARD

SANDRA DEE

NORMAN WISDOM

6
Films

I went to so many films – most of them pretty dire too! There were lots of cinemas in Kingston then, but each only had one screen. The Granada and the Regal and the Empire were all perfectly respectable, but Kingston Kinema was a total fleapit. It showed arty, less mainstream films, and we sometimes went there too, though we weren't supposed to.

The Kinema attracted Dirty Old Men – far dirtier than the ones who hung around Maxwells music shop. The pitch-black of the Kinema made them bold. They'd shuffle along the empty rows and sit right next to you. You'd strain as far away from them as possible, staring up at the screen, heart thumping. You'd keep telling yourself it was going to be fine, he wouldn't *do* anything, but then a clammy hand, repulsive as a jellyfish, would slither onto your knee. You'd jerk your knee away from it, trembling, but you knew that hand would come back. Sometimes it changed into a crab and tried to scuttle underneath your skirt. Then at long long last this would galvanize you into action and you'd grab your friend and sidle down the row away from him.

Why on earth did we put up with this? Why didn't we complain loudly and go and find an usherette? We were all as hopeless as each other – Carol, Chris, all my other friends: we sat paralysed with shame and fear while these hateful men dabbed at us disgustingly. It was as if *we'd* done something bad and embarrassing. We might joke about it afterwards, even getting fits of the giggles, but at the time it was terrifying.

So why did we *go* to the Kinema? Well, we wanted to see those arty movies, a lot of them X-rated. They would probably be considered very bland kids' stuff nowadays. We were so totally innocent, even a Cliff Richard film could shock us. We all wanted to see his new film, *Expresso Bongo*, because it was set in Soho where all the strip joints were.

Friday 22 January
In the evening I went to see 'Expresso Bongo' with Carol at the Regal. We saw tons of girls from school there, all dressed up pretending to be sixteen. Jill, Susan and Joyce were there in the 'ninepennies' and Jill told me afterwards that she had seen Peter there and he had smiled at her. She also said that Joyce had asked Susan and her to club together and

buy some cigarettes. They reluctantly agreed, but Susan wouldn't smoke any. Jill had three and wasn't very impressed, but Joyce finished the lot off! I think she's only 13!
P.S. 'Expresso Bongo' was very good.

I was too shy to write in my diary about the astonishing scene set in a Soho club where you saw topless showgirls. There was an audible gasp from the cinema audience as this line of girls jiggled across the screen. They weren't even entirely topless: they had little stars in pertinent places, presumably stuck on. It must have been pretty painful removing them each night.

You didn't get topless models in newspapers in 1960, not the papers we had at home anyway. You didn't get girly magazines openly displayed on newsagents' shelves either. The only bare breasts I'd ever seen were on African women in the *National Geographic* magazine. Those *Expresso Bongo* girls made a big impression on all of us. We talked about them excitedly at school the next morning.

Mostly our film-going was a lot less adventurous. I seemed very easy to please. On Monday 4 January I went to see Tommy Steele in *Tommy the Toreador* and pronounced this film 'very good.' The next day I saw Norman Wisdom in *Follow a Star*, which I said was 'very funny'. You would have to tie me to my seat to get me to watch either film now.

Carol and I went to the pictures two or three times a week in the holidays. We went after school too, sometimes with Sue and Cherry. They lived in Kingston too. Sue literally lived next door to me, at number eleven Cumberland House, where we'd both lived since we were six.

This was 'a better class of council estate', according to my mother – and she did her level best to bring me up a better class of child. Sue's mother, Nancy, was equally ambitious for her daughter. No other children in Cumberland House had such white socks and blouses, such polished brown sandals, such expensive school satchels.

Sue and Nancy had heated arguments nowadays. Nancy wouldn't let Sue use make-up and still liked her to wear smocked Viyella dresses with long blue socks and flat shoes, whereas we were all allowed lipstick and eyeshadow, nylons and little heels. Sue secretly used her birthday money on her own lipstick and nylons and spent two minutes in the ladies' toilets each time she went out, turning herself into a teenager.

Cherry lived in a flat too, but it was part of a very large house further down the road. When she was a little girl she'd had a pageboy haircut, but now she had a blonde ponytail that bounced as she walked. Cherry was part of a different teenage world altogether. She went riding, she joined a tennis club, she sang in amateur Gilbert and Sullivan productions. (Biddy perversely sneered at these harmless middle-class hobbies.)

I'd been friends with Sue and Cherry when we were children but they'd gone to different secondary schools. However, now we were in the third year (Year Nine), Coombe had expanded and Sue and Cherry started going there too.

Thursday 4 February
After school I went to the pictures with Sue and Cherry. Carol still has a chill. It was 'Please Turn Over', and all three of us enjoyed it very much. Julia Lockwood was in it who I quite like. In the film she wrote a book called 'Naked Revolt' about her suburban family, with some shocking results. It showed you excerpts from the book, and I would have given anything to have been able to read it. The other film was good too; it was called 'The Desperate Man'. Conrad Phillips (William Tell) was in it, and also a very attractive girl called Jill Ireland.

You got good value for money going to the

pictures in 1960. There were always two films, the main feature film and then a shorter film, usually a thriller. In between you got Pathé News, introduced by a noisy cockerel, and a ten-minute documentary called *Look at Life*. If you had nothing else to do, you could sit there in your red plush seat watching the entire programme all over again. You'd only have to get up when they played the National Anthem. It sounds so strange now, but they truly did play 'God Save the Queen' after every cinema performance, and everyone stood to attention, looking solemn.

Thursday 11 February
After school I dashed home and changed, slapped some powder and lipstick on my face, called for Sue, and then we went to the flicks. We met Carol there and saw 'A Summer Place' with Sandra Dee and Troy Donahue. It was quite good, but a little too dramatic. Everyone seemed to have a love affair with someone else, and crept hand in hand to the boat house, beach or park respectively. It was rather like a women's magazine story, taking you to the bedroom door and no further.

I don't think I knew much about what happened

behind the bedroom door at fourteen, but I wanted to sound sophisticated.

I nearly always went to the pictures with my friends. Harry had taken me when I was a little girl but we didn't go anywhere together now. I *did* occasionally go with Biddy:

Saturday 13 February
Mum said she wanted to see the film 'The Reluctant Debutante' so we went together. On the way we went into the Bentalls' record department. I saw P. Wilson and Y. McCarthy in turquoise duffel coats, extremely tight jeans and cha-cha shoes being cuddled by a group of horrible spotty teddy boys. 'The Reluctant Debutante' was very good, and Mum and I also enjoyed the other film 'Watusi' very much.

Oh dear, it would have been *so* much cooler to be wearing a duffel coat and tight jeans and cuddling a teddy boy rather than going to the cinema with my mum.

The following Saturday I 'went to see "Pillow Talk" with Carol and Sue'. *Pillow Talk sounds* sophisticated, but it was a frothy comedy. I vastly preferred the next film I saw, *The Nun's Story*, with Audrey Hepburn. Audrey made thousands of girls decide they wanted to be nuns, although sadly no *real* nun ever looked so ethereally exquisite in her veil and wimple. I fell in love with Audrey like everyone else, but the nun's vow of obedience appalled me.

Monday 22 February
In the evening I met Carol and we went to see 'The Nun's Story'. It was a really wonderful film, one of the best I've seen. It showed you what a nun's life is really like. I know one thing, and that is that I would never make a good nun, not even a makeshift one. Never, never could I have such sheer obedience; if I think I am right I cannot obey humbly but I <u>must</u> argue my point. But humility is the quality I lack most. If anyone says anything humiliating to me, something inside me is hurt and angry and tells me to hit back at that person with cutting remarks. Besides, I could not bear a life minus men and children.

I saw delicious melodramas like *Conspiracy of Hearts* with Carol – but occasionally I went to a comedy with Chris. We saw *Please Don't Eat the Daisies* – and sang '*Please, please,* don't *eat the daisies*' up and down Coombe's corridors for weeks afterwards. We had a lovely cosy day when we went to see *School for Scoundrels*.

Thursday 19 May
I went home with Chris at dinner time. It was raining, and we had to wait for 4 buses. When we eventually got to the Keepings' we were absolutely <u>*drenched*</u>*. For dinner we had liver, baked beans, cauliflower and new potatoes; then rhubarb and evaporated milk!* <u>*Very nice!*</u> *Then we did our maths together, and then caught the train to Kingston, and saw 'School for Scoundrels'. It was very funny, but Chris and I laughed far more at the other film which was meant to be VERY SERIOUS. The main character was called Julian Caesar, his best friend Marc Antony, another friend Brutus, his girlfriend Portia, and his enemy Cassius.* <u>*How daft*</u>*.*

It could well have been a brilliant contemporary reworking of Shakespeare but clearly it didn't work for us! We must have infuriated everyone sitting near us, going giggle giggle giggle, but only half the audience seemed interested in watching the film:

Sitting in front of us were these girls and teds snogging (if you'll pardon the vulgar expression)

*and Chris and I are positive that one of them (the
one on the end without a boy) was Jennifer D!*

Oh dear, how awful to be the one on the end
without a boy!

I wasn't a particularly religious girl, but I adored
the film *The Ten Commandments*. In an age long
before videos and DVDs it was a rare treat to find
a film repeated after its original release. I saw *The
Ten Commandments* was on again at the cinema
and begged Carol to go with me.

It was extremely long, but we watched
enraptured. It was filmed very solemnly, with
the actors frequently standing still as if in a
tableau, gesturing bizarrely, but we soon got used
to that. It was very stirring when they were
building the pyramids and Moses saved the old
woman – she's actually his real mother but he
didn't know this.

The colours of *The Ten Commandments* were so
rich and beautiful and the miracles themselves
seemed wondrous. In our age of computer-
generated trickery the parting of the Red Sea would
probably seem pretty pathetic – but I held my
breath when Charlton Heston made his way
through those waves. The whole cinema whispered,
'*How did they* do *that?*'

The film was about the very good and the very

bad – and I'm afraid I was mostly on the bad guy's side. I thought irreverently that the film's Voice of God was a little like the voice of the Wizard of Oz. I quite liked Charlton Heston as Moses but I vastly preferred his enemy, Yul Brynner, playing bald, sexy Rameses, who was unhappily married to dark, scheming Nefertiri. She was one hundred per cent a baddie, a callous murderer, but Anne Baxter, who played her, was so beautiful that I thought her wonderful. I didn't want to be blonde Susan Wooldridge any more. I wanted to be dark and sultry with long shiny black hair and crimson lips.

I went to some classic adaptations with the wrong attitude entirely. Carol and I hadn't read D. H. Lawrence's *Sons and Lovers* (and *Lady Chatterley's Lover* hadn't even been published yet) but we thought it would be pretty sexy. We watched the film restlessly and grew impatient at the end.

'What a swizzle. It wasn't a *bit* sexy,' I said. 'I don't think much of D. H. Lawrence.'

But sometimes these adaptations worked wonders.

Saturday 23 July
In the afternoon I went to the flicks again, this time with Sue, and saw 'Wuthering Heights', on at the

Kinema. It was very good, and at the end I could hear Sue sniffling away as if her heart was broken. I think I will read the book, as it is one of the classics Miss Pierce told us to read.

I read it that summer, waking up early every morning and reading for hours until I reached that beautiful last paragraph.

7

Books

I read voraciously right through my teens. I didn't read teenage books: there were no such things in those days. Well, there *was* a small shelf in the library labelled TEENAGE BOOKS, but they were dull-as-ditchwater career books with ridiculous titles like *Donald is a Dentist* and *Vera is a Vet.* Donald and Vera were barely characterized and there was no plot whatsoever. Each book was a dreary account of how to pursue the relevant career. I didn't want to give people fillings or spay cats so I left them gathering dust on the shelf. (I *might* have been tempted by *Jacky is a Journalist.*)

I read children's books up to the age of eleven or so and then I switched to adult books. I didn't just read classics like *Wuthering Heights,* of course. I read all sorts of books – some trashy, some tremendous, some wildly unsuitable.

I spent most of my pocket money on paperbacks and borrowed three books from the library every week, sometimes twice a week. If I was particularly interested or irritated by a book I wrote about it in my diary, but sadly I didn't record every book I read. That would have been like writing 'Today I brushed my teeth with Colgate toothpaste', something I simply took for granted as part of my daily life.

I had various favourite books and I read these again and again. I kept my bright pink Pan paperback of *The Diary of Anne Frank* on my bedside table, with a carefully cut-out photograph of Anne pinned above my bed. The Holocaust had happened less than twenty years before. I could barely take it in. It seemed so unbelievably terrible that Anne and six million others had lost their lives because they were Jews.

I thought of her as a martyr but she was certainly no saint. I loved reading the passages in her diary when she complained bitterly about her mother and longed for a proper boyfriend. But as I said in the first chapter, it was her diary entries about writing that meant the most to me and I learned them by heart. I mentioned my other all-time favourite book in the first chapter too: *I Capture the Castle* by Dodie Smith.

It's the story of Cassandra and her sister Rose, living in poverty in a dilapidated castle with their writer father and eccentric stepmother, Topaz; then two rich American brothers come to live nearby . . .

It sounds absolute toffee, a ridiculous romantic fairytale, but trust me, it's a wonderful book and Cassandra is such an endearing and compelling narrator that you are swept into the story and believe every single word of it.

I didn't just envy Cassandra her two-guinea red-leather notebook. I wanted to dab myself with her bluebell scent and drink green crème de menthe and swim in a moat at midnight.

I loved reading *sad* stories. I found *The Wind Cannot Read* wondrously moving:

Tuesday 2 February
Morris and Iris [friends of Biddy's] *have lent me 'The Wind Cannot Read', by Richard Mason, author of my favourite 'The World of Suzie Wong'. I'm enjoying it very much at the moment.*

Wednesday 3 February
I finished reading 'The Wind Cannot Read'. It is a lovely book, but very sad at the end. I almost cried, and I'm definitely not the sentimental type.

I'm sure I'd remain dry-eyed if I ever tried to plough through it now, but one book that would still make me cry is *The Story of Gabrielle*.

Tuesday 23 February
I went to the library and got 3 books. I have finished
one already called 'The Story of Gabrielle'. It is a
wonderful story of a truly amazing child who dies
of cancer. It is very moving, and I really love and
admire Gabby.

The Story of Gabrielle was beautifully and
movingly written by Gabrielle's mother. I own it
now but can't even bring myself to look at it
because I find it unbearable to read about the death
of a child, maybe because I've known so many
special children who have died of cancer. Over the
years I've made many visits to sick children who
have written to me. They are always very brave so
I try hard to be brave too, though when I get home
I often cry.

I know *I* sometimes write sad books now. I wept
when I wrote *Kiss* – and I cried and cried when I
wrote the last chapter of *My Sister Jodie*. I tried
hard not to let *Vicky Angel* be too upsetting, even
though it was very sad. I cut out one of the early
chapters, with detailed descriptions of Vicky
in hospital.

I was certainly wary of hospital scenes in fiction
back in 1960:

Wednesday 3 February
I carried on reading [after finishing *The Wind Cannot Read*] *'Not As a Stranger', but I'm not going to read it any more. First it told you about digging a boil out of a neck and the pus etc. etc., and it made me feel sick, and then a little boy cuts off his w— with a razor blade. Ugh! I very nearly was sick then, and I'm not going near the horrible book again.*

I read historical fiction too. I had a thing about Queen Elizabeth I in my early teens and read anything I could find about her and the times she lived in.

Wednesday 20 January
I got a good book out of the library called 'Young Bess' by Margaret Irwin. It is all about Elizabeth 1st when she was about 12–15. She wasn't half advanced for her age! There is a portrait of her in the book painted when she was 13. She looked at least 18! Also Tom Seymour, a man of over thirty, was in love with her! I can't imagine a man loving me like that at this age.

Thursday 21 January
I'm enjoying 'Young Bess' very much. It makes you

think of Elizabeth as if she was still living. The book is very witty, but you have to use your brains to understand the jokes.

Tuesday 17 May
After school I went to the library. I got a very interesting book about Elizabethans. I specially enjoyed the chapters about cosmetics and ailments. It's amazing that the Elizabethans managed to live at all! They used to put cerise (white lead) on face, neck and chest, which slowly turned the skin withered, and gave the women gastro-intestinal diseases and palsy. They put rouge on cheeks and lips that simply ate into the flesh after a time. Also, if they had scars, spots or freckles they put on this ointment that destroyed all skin tissue, which, naturally, left horrible scars. So the Elizabethans put on more and more ointment to get rid of the scars until they had hardly any skin left at all.

I wished we studied the Elizabethans in history. I sat next to a funny, lively, dark-haired girl called Jill in history lessons and we bonded terrifically when she said she hero-worshipped Elizabeth too.

Tuesday 1 March
Had double History. Mr Stokes looked at Jill's library book and roared with laughter when he saw it was entitled 'Lovers of my Lord Admiral'. Jill explained that she was an Elizabeth fan, and when Mr S. looked at my book and saw it was 'The Bright Pavilions' (an Eliz. Book) he realised I was too.

Jill was more flexible than me when it came to periods of history.

Friday 12 February
Jill lent me a book 'Our Dearest Emma' by Lozania Prole. Never have I read a book in which there are so many different romances. I am sure Emy, when she was alive, found it difficult to keep track of so many bedfellows.

Biddy didn't mind me reading about historical bed-hopping, but she did fuss about contemporary sexy books. Sandra, a girl I knew at dancing classes, told me that *'Peyton Place* was a shocking book, her friend had showed it to her at school. I asked Mum if I could read it but she said wait till you're 16.'

I didn't waste time arguing. I knew Biddy wouldn't let me buy it and I wasn't sure the staid librarians in Kingston library would let me check it out. So I secretly borrowed *Peyton Place* from Sandra.

Wednesday 13 April
This morning I phoned Cherry to arrange about the flicks, and then spent a good half hour reading 'Peyton Place' which is <u>strictly taboo</u>. *As I flipped through I found the interesting bits Sandra referred to, but oh, what a storm in a teacup! The parts about Alison's adolescence are a little boring, as in thousands of books it mentions, sometimes being far more frank, these things. I thought Stella conceiving her stepfather's baby a little peculiar, but when it told you about Betty's seduction, and her tight shorts being easy to slip off, well, I thought it sheer trash. In fact I had a good laugh to think that sensible adults are 'shocked' by this 'outspoken book'. I think my dear parents would get a shock if they knew some of the books I read that are far worse.*

Thursday 14 April
This morning I finished skimming through 'Peyton Place'. It went on in the same manner as before, ending up when Alison finally launches upon 'The

Fate Worse Than Death', and discovers that she loves Peyton Place and is no longer afraid of it.

The next day was Good Friday – and I wanted something else to keep me going all over the Easter weekend. My longest book was *Gone with the Wind*, over a thousand pages, but for some reason I'd lent it to Uncle Ron – Biddy's friend, not a real uncle.

Friday 15 April
I phoned Ron up to ask him if he was coming over on Saturday. He said he definitely was so I asked if he would return my book 'Gone with the Wind' when he came. He promised he would, then I rang off after chattering a little. I hope he does remember to bring it as I am stuck over the weekend without any books to read, as I have either finished my library books or else they're boring. I cannot bear persevering with a book when I don't like it.

Re-reading *Gone with the Wind* kept me going right through Easter and beyond. I guzzled my chocolate eggs and then tried to suck my tummy in, sighing over Scarlett O'Hara's minuscule waist. I didn't envy her any of her men. I didn't even care for Rhett Butler – but I *did* envy Scarlett her green velvet gown and all her rustling petticoats.

Ga and Biddy and I all unusually agreed that *Gone with the Wind* was a great read. We all also liked Monica Dickens.

Friday 8 April
I finished reading 'Joy and Josephine' by Monica Dickens. It was a <u>very</u> good book, with a really smashing plot.

I spent the day at my grandma's on 20 April, helping her with the spring cleaning at Fassett Road.

Ga armed me with a ladder, a rag, and a bucket of hot water and Flash. I washed down all the upstairs doors and frameworks, then all the banisters, both the landing and the stairs, and the cupboard door, and all that enormous panel, and in all the little crevices where dirt miraculously collects. Ga was very pleased, and paid me 4 bob! Then after a fish and chips lunch (home cooked) Ga and I lay out in the sun in deckchairs. My, it was as warm as the middle of Summer. I stayed out there so long that

I regretfully finished reading a very funny book.
'One Pair of Feet' by Monica Dickens.

I met Monica Dickens many years later, when we were both judging a children's writing competition, and I shyly told her how much I'd enjoyed her books. She was lovely to me, but a terrible stickler for correct grammar and punctuation while judging those children's stories, worse than any teacher!

Ga owned very few books herself, and she didn't belong to the public library. She had a subscription to Boots library and fed her reading habit that way. Sometimes she lent me her library books too.

My father brought me books from Westminster library. He worked at the nearby Treasury. He was such a strange man. He could be so moody and unpredictable, losing his temper violently and then sulking, sometimes for weeks. He rarely chatted with me and never tried to understand me – and yet he had an unerring knack for picking out unusual books for me that I *loved*.

It was through Harry that I discovered Rumer Godden, a favourite author of mine for many years. He brought *The River* home for me first, a beautiful bittersweet story of a family in India, narrated by thirteen-year-old Harriet, who wants to be a writer.

It took me a few pages to get into the story. I was a little dismayed to see the Latin declensions and conjugations for *love* and *war* on the first page. I hated Latin lessons even more than maths – but wonderfully, Harriet seemed equally hopeless at Latin.

I read *The River* over and over, begging Harry to renew it for me. He then found Rumer Godden's *The Greengage Summer* on the library shelves, and I liked this even more. I identified with Cecil this time and suffered painfully with her. I was angry with her elder sister, Joss. I envied Joss her beauty and confidence. I especially envied her because Eliot was attracted to her. I adored Eliot, even when it turned out he was a criminal.

The Greengage Summer was a story about children but it was told in the most adult way. It was wonderful when I bought my own copy with my pocket money. I could read it whenever I wanted. I soon knew the first paragraph off by heart. It starts: 'On and off, all that hot French August, we made ourselves ill from eating the greengages' – and on and off, all that year when I was fourteen in 1960, I read that book until it seeped into my soul.

I don't think I've ever read as widely as I did then. If I particularly liked a library book I'd copy out appealing passages and then stick them into my diary.

Wednesday 30 March
I got a good book from the library called 'Dress
Rehearsal' by Monica Sterling. Parts of it are
boring, but the rest is very, very good. I like chapter
seven best, about Olive, an Irish girl, who first
obtained Jocelyn's admiration by shouting at her
teacher 'Oh you and your damn Girl Guides.'

There are then two pages of weeny biro writing
to remind me why I liked it so much. It looks
embarrassingly mawkish now.

However, I did occasionally show good taste in
literature. Harry bought a copy of Vladimir
Nabokov's *Lolita*, a very controversial literary
novel much tutted over in Biddy's *Daily Mail*. It
was the story of a middle-aged man who runs away
with a twelve-year-old girl, a subject justifiably
considered shocking. I was told I was far too young
to read it. Harry started it at once but gave up
after the first chapter.

'It's not really my sort of thing,' he said, and
handed it over to Biddy. I wrote in my diary: 'At
the moment Mummy is sitting with her nose buried
in the book taking in every word!' There were
rather too many obscure baroque words for Biddy's
taste. She abandoned *Lolita* just a few pages in too.

'It's stupid, all this fancy stuff. You can't tell

what he's on about,' she said. She skimmed through the book, pausing here and there. 'There doesn't seem anything in it anyway.'

'Then can *I* read it?' I asked.

'No, you can't! And you wouldn't understand a word of it anyway,' said Biddy.

Again I didn't argue. I waited until I was in our flat on my own, and then I flew to the bookcase and started reading – and reading and reading and reading. It was a revelation. I hadn't known language could be used in such a rich and elegant way. I whispered each sentence, tasting the words on my tongue.

I knew I simply *had* to read the whole novel. I was a fast reader but I couldn't possibly whiz through it before Biddy came home from work. The dust jacket was a distinct brown, with the word LOLITA in enormous capitals on the front. The solution was simple. I took the cover off, and swapped it for a Catherine Cookson novel of a similar size.

I took my disguised copy of *Lolita* everywhere, reading it at the tea table, on the bus, in the playground. If any of my friends glanced curiously over my shoulder, they didn't see anything on the page to make them gasp or giggle. It wasn't a so-called 'dirty book', one to pass round with all the rude pages carefully marked with old bus tickets. Humbert and Lolita were alarmingly *real*.

Lolita was very like some of the tough, pretty, scary girls at school and I thought I understood why Humbert was so enchanted by her. I wasn't particularly shocked, just enormously interested. It's strange, nowadays I find the whole story so troubling, so distressingly offensive, that I can't bear to read it. I strongly recommend that you don't read it either. It's truly not a book for children.

Very occasionally a child *wrote* a book that got published. When I was nine or ten I'd enjoyed reading Pamela Brown's *The Swish of the Curtain*, written in her early teens. I was very impressed – but there was a good five-year gap between us then. But that June when I was fourteen I borrowed a book called *Strange Evil* from the library.

Monday 13 June
At the moment I'm reading a book by a fourteen-year-old, Jane Gaskell. The girl's a genius. She must be terribly mature for her age: I won't be ready to attempt to write a book for at least another four years.

I don't know why I wrote that. I seemed to be starting to write a book almost every week of 1960 – starting, but never finishing!

TEACH YOURSELF
TO WRITE

K. BETTERTON

8
Writing

I was often inspired to write by the book I was currently reading.

Saturday 16 January
I did a little homework like a good girl and then read some more of 'I Capture the Castle' by Dodie Smith. It is a very good book. I also started writing a story. It has its possibilities.

Sunday 17 January
I continued writing my story. I'm quite pleased with it. The trouble is that I'm neglecting my homework because of it.

I wish I'd said what the story was *about*. I wrote hundreds of thousands of words when I was twelve, thirteen, fourteen, fifteen . . . and they've nearly all vanished now. I threw them out myself, ashamed because they were so childish, so awkward, so derivative. Biddy frequently had a purge of my possessions too in one of her regular spring cleans. Once or twice as I got older she sneakily read something that infuriated or offended her in my diaries and journals and notebooks and she threw them down the rubbish chute.

However, she didn't ever throw any of my writing away if it was in a school notebook, so *The Story of Latina* survived. Maybe Biddy thought it was an English project rather than my own private scribbling. I think I'd probably stolen the big blue notebook from the school stationery cupboard.

At the top of the first page I wrote in capitals 'A BOOK OF TEN STORIES FOR TEENAGERS' which seemed overly ambitious. I only managed thirteen pages and three lines of the first story, and that was mostly preliminary passages before Latina herself came into the story. *Latina!* Why did I make up such a weird name? I didn't like Latin, I hated it. I suppose Latina was one stage better than Mathematica! I just had time for a detailed description of Latina before I lost interest in the story.

Her eyes gazed into his, a soft, intelligent bright blue, which reminded him very much of the sea for although they were now calm and peaceful they had tints of violet, green, grey and black which showed they could change colour in accordance to her mood. They appeared big in her pointed sensitive face which was framed with a tumble of dark straight hair that fell in a cascade past her shoulders. She was of average height as far as he could judge, and slim. Her skin was a golden tan and she wore a faded cotton dress.

I rather think I must have based Latina on a clay model of a girl's head that I'd had as a holiday present from St Ives. I called *her* Tasmania (goodness knows why – I think I just wanted it to sound exotic) and kept her on my bedside table. While I did my homework or wrote my stories, my hand would reach out and I'd stroke Tasmania's shiny black hair, smooth her arched clay eyebrows, and finger her pointed chin.

Now here she was, re-christened with an even odder name and given an indeterminate age. I had her at fourteen at first, but I clearly intended her to have a full-blooded romance with my hero so I added another three years to make it more respectable.

I called my hero Alan. I was still feeling very fond of the Alan who had been my boyfriend when I was in Year Six at Latchmere, my primary school. My fictional Alan was a grown man, not a young boy, and, as the opening pages make clear, going through a pretty traumatic time. I'll embarrass myself and give you another quote:

As soon as Alan found out, after thinking for a while and knowing that he could not keep it a secret, he notified the authorities and then returned home. He undressed and had a shower and a shave, and redressed in clean underwear, clean blue open-necked shirt and navy trousers, and an old windcheater. His socks were also clean, and his sandals well polished. A knife in a sheath was fixed to his belt, a comb, handkerchief, map, wallet and some chocolate went into his trouser pockets and his windcheater pockets were filled with a packet of sandwiches, and two bottles, one containing brandy and one of plain water. He then packed a small case with a change of clothes, pyjamas and washing things.

He glanced around at his small flat littered with possessions, and a surge of affection for it rose in his breast. He moved towards the mantelpiece and tenderly picked up a photo of an attractive, smiling girl and kissed it. Then he replaced it gently and moved slowly towards the door. What would Barbara say when she knew, he wondered? What would they all say? He paused with his hand on

*the door knob. Suddenly he leant on the wall
and closed his eyes. Yes, what would his friends
say? Would they despise him, use his name as a
revolting word? He pressed his knuckles against
his eyes so that all he could see was a revolving
whirl of darkness. Through this he could clearly
see the faces of his friends, Barbara, his boss, his
parents. All were pointing at him, accusing him,
wrinkling their noses in distaste. Was it so terrible?
Did it make all that difference? He savagely
gnawed at his knuckle. All right, he would
show them. Damn them all, what did they matter?
What did anyone matter? Barbara floated into his
mind, and a sob rose in his throat and choked him.
Never again would he be able to hold her in his
arms, or never firmly shake a man's hand.
Thinking of hand shakes he tentatively glanced
down at his own hand, his right one. A tear
glistened for an instant on his tanned cheek, but
it was wiped away as quickly as it had come. The
clock struck the hour. Alan straightened himself,
his ears strained to the door. Sure enough, just as
the nine chimes had died away there came a long
firm ringing on the doorbell. Although his face was
now pale, it was composed. He took a quick last
glance around the room, and then flung open the
door. There stood two burly men dressed in black
suits, shirts, shoes and hats. Alan swallowed,*

105

picked up his case, and then stepped on to the landing and closed the front door behind him. 'I am ready,' he said almost inaudibly. The men put on black rubber gloves and then stood either side of Alan holding his arms in their firm cruel grasp. They marched him slowly along the streets to the city's dock. As they went passers by stood and stared and the youths laughed and shouted in derision. Alan clenched his teeth and tried to shut his eyes to the jeers. A few of the onlookers felt sorry for this brave handsome young man who stood so erect, and whose set face did not give way to his grief. Only a few days ago he had been one of those ordinary people, who now stood and stared at him. But he had never been one of the mob of onlookers because he had felt only pity for the miserable wretches taken by the black police. One of the youths threw a stone, and its sharp edge cut Alan's cheek. He flinched, but his face was still set. Whatever happened his pride would not let him relax his face from the composed mask, or to falter his steady step, although his mind was in a terrible ferment. Oh God, he thought, let it be over soon. Let me get on the boat. Oh God, let this Hellish walk be over soon. The black police's hands gripped right into his arms bruising the flesh, and the blood from the cut started to trickle down his cheek.

OK, let's play guessing games. Why has poor Alan in his clean outfit, old windcheater and polished sandals (!) been manhandled onto this boat by the black police? After passing out on the boat all night Alan regains consciousness in the morning.

When Alan awoke the first thing he saw was three eyes staring into his. He started, and realised that his life with The Disease had begun. Just as there had been Bubonic Plague in the Middle Ages, in the twentieth century there was also a disease, but in many ways a more deadly one although it did not cause death, and was not infectious. It was a disease which, if one caught it, would make one grow another part of the body. In Alan's case it was not so bad because he had only grown another finger on his right hand, but others grew another leg, arm, eyes, nose, ear, sometimes even another head. The authorities formed a party of men called the black police named thus because of their black uniform, who were responsible for finding the disformed men and women. The men were sent to a far off island to the west and the women to a far off island in the east. They were not allowed to go to the same island because a man and a woman might fall in love and have children who would naturally be

107

disformed. The authorities naturally had to be very careful about this, because if it was allowed to happen there might become a whole race of badly disformed people.

This seems a startling idea for me to have thought up. I'd be quite proud if it was original – but I'd read John Wyndham's brilliant science fiction book *The Chrysalids*, where the characters also sprout extra digits or endure other deformities and are rounded up and sent to the badlands. John Wyndham manages to make his scenario convincing. A few of his characters discover they can read each other's thoughts. This has always seemed such an appealing idea that from time to time I've tried to do this with people I'm very close to, even though it's probably scientifically impossible.

Perhaps it was just as well I didn't develop the relationship between my six-fingered Alan and sensitive Latina or we'd all get the giggles. I don't think I *ever* finished a story when I was fourteen, but it didn't stop me trying again and again. On 5 February I wrote: 'Cherry sold me a lovely black file for only a bob.' A bob was slang for a shilling – that's 5p in today's money. 'I'm going to get cracking on a new story now.'

I was always happy to do any kind of writing, even English essay homework.

Friday 19 February
Miss Pierce was the only one to give us weekend homework; all the other teachers let us off because next Monday and Tuesday are half-term. Luckily I adore English Essay so I'm not complaining, but it's a damn shame for the others. The subject is 'The Village Street' and Miss P requests some vivid description. I wish we had a really decent subject to write about, most of my essays have to be so childish. Oh, how I long to get a book published, just to show Miss P. I have one in mind at the moment, a rather sordid story about teenagers. I long to shock Miss P and show her that her quiet shy Jacky isn't what she thinks she is.

I used the word 'damn', which sounds quaint now, but when I was fourteen it was the worst four-letter word any of us used out loud (though we might whisper or spell out the really bad ones).

When I was a little girl I took great delight in buying fashion pattern books with my pocket money. I'd cut out all the particularly interesting girls and ladies and invent elaborate games for them. I was still doing this when I was a 'big' girl.

I justified this by insisting it was for legitimate writing inspiration – and sometimes it worked.

On Tuesday 23 February I wrote:

Yesterday at dinnertime I bought a fashion book, and the people I cut out of it today have given me a wonderful idea for a book. It is set in the future and . . . Oh I won't go into details, it is sufficient to say that at the moment I think it is a good idea.

I've no idea whether I wrote it or not – I can't remember it. I'm interested that I don't want to go into details about it in my diary. I feel exactly the same way now. If I get a good idea it's fatal to talk about it, and even writing too many notes can destroy it. Story ideas need to stay in my head, gently glowing in the dark, developing for a long time before they're ready for the light of day. I like the wise note of caution even though I'm obviously bubbling over with enthusiasm: '*at the moment* I think it's a good idea'. So often today's sparkling and original idea seems tarnished and second-rate the next day!

I bought another big fashion book in April – and the *following* April, when I was fifteen and going out with my first steady boyfriend, I wrote: 'I still haven't managed to grow out of buying fashion books, and cutting out the people and making families of them.' My handwriting is more like a five-year-old's than a fifteen-year-old's on this page but I add: 'By the way, excuse the occasional left hand writing, but I am putting nail varnish on and I don't want it smudged.'

I'm impressed that I was reasonably ambidextrous then. I've just had a go at writing left-handed now and find it very difficult. It would be such a *useful* thing to be able to do, especially when I've got a very long queue of girls wanting their books signed. My right hand starts to ache horribly after an hour or so. It would be wonderful to be able to swap my pen to the other hand and give the right one a rest.

Later that April of 1960 I told Chris I still loved playing with my fashion book:

She seemed shocked – and I must admit it does sound a bit queer – a grown girl of fifteen playing with cut-out figures. No-one but me knows the enjoyment I get out of it though, and also playing around is some constructive use. Each model has a special character and personality – I don't have to invent this, it just comes. Then when I'm writing a story I've got a lot of ready made characters complete with names. I especially like the 'Style' fashion books – the drawings are clear and attractive and a lot of the figures have very strong personalities. I'm not talking rubbish; it's true. As I've been playing with fashion books ever since I've been about six I have some very firm favourites that have lasted through the years although most of the old ones aren't included now as they're too old-fashioned.

Judging by the following diary entry my fashion-book games and stories weren't childish at all – quite the opposite: 'Yesterday I had a lovely morning in bed with my fashion book. I discovered a lovely new person, Carola.' I can *remember* Carola – she had long hair, and as the fashion artist wanted to show off the unusual waist on her tight skirt he drew her without a blouse top. So there she was, as bold as brass in her bra and skirt and high heels. I obviously felt she was what Biddy called 'fast'. So I wrote:

I've decided she can have an affair with John, and I've given her Betty and Katy to look after. [They were small girls with very carefully cut-out pigtails. Did I cast Carola as a single mum with two daughters already?] *She goes around with Nicky and Sherry's crowd. I spent three contented hours with my fashion book.*

The next day:

I bought myself a lovely hard 2H pencil, a thing I've been wanting for a long time. I drew a picture of Carola, Nick, Katy and Betty from memory. I know you should use a soft pencil for drawing, but I hate dark smudgy messy lines, and much prefer neat precise lines. Also the children look much more delicate with a hard line. I want to write about Carola etc., etc.

The drawing and the story and the fashion books were all thrown away but they've stayed indelibly clear in my mind to this day.

I used my own life as inspiration as well as all my paper girls. On 1 March Miss Pierce, our English teacher, told us all about people who lived on barges (in preparation for introducing *Maiden's Trip* by Emma Smith as our class reader). I wrote: 'It was interesting and worth keeping in mind for a story, except that I have just started one

113

about a co-ed school based on my many <u>experiances</u> at Latchmere.'

I spelled experiences wrong and underlined it heavily. I'm not sure what extraordinary experiences I was thinking of. I'd obviously got fed up with it five days later, because on Sunday 6 March I wrote: 'I started writing a story, but got a bit fed up with it.' That could be a valid diary entry nowadays, though now I just grit my teeth and carry on writing – on and on and on – until six months later the story is finished, polished, typed out and sent off to my publishers.

At least now I can reassure myself that I've produced a lot of novels that children enjoy reading. When I was fourteen I was plagued with doubts about my writing.

I wrote in March:

Is it just a form of escapism? Am I burying my head in the sand like an ostrich, is my writing just an adolescent craze? No, it <u>can't</u> be just a phase. Well, I've settled it that at least I'm serious about my writing. But is it any good? Is it? Oh, how I wish I knew. I have a reasonable grasp of writing, <u>but</u> am I any good? I mean <u>really</u> good? I just don't know. I want very much to prove to myself that I can write good material. I would like <u>very</u> much to

114

hold a finished story in my hands. So I am not going to be weak-willed and sit here wishing, I'm going to think of a plot and – START WRITING! Blast homework, blast everything, I <u>must</u> prove it to myself. Oh let me think of a good plot, some realistic characters, and let me produce a really good book.

I was so frantic, so earnest. It's a relief to flip the page in my diary and read:

We had a really <u>stinking</u> sum to do for Geometry homework. Chris and I just sat back and laughed it got so complicated. I've now cooled off from my writing outburst yesterday, but I am still determined to write a good novel. Imagine the sheer bliss of printing 'THE END' on the umpteenth sheet of manuscript paper.

A week later I wrote:

Remember my writing outburst on Wed 9th? Well, I have thought of a really good idea for a novel, using my own experience – so that I can know what

I'm writing about. Now I must get on and – WRITE.

The next Sunday we went to visit my godparents, Gladys and Sid, who had just adopted three-year-old twins. I wrote that night:

Gladys says their mother is married, but the children are from another man. How can she just abandon them? They are such lovely pretty kids, perfectly healthy, happy and normal [obviously *not* little Tracy Beakers!]. *The mother idea could be a new angle for a book . . .*

I was brimming with new ideas, new angles. On Saturday 2 April 'I bought a red fat shilling exercise book for my new story. It is coming along nicely at the moment.'

I wasn't limiting myself just to novels:

Reading a good book has brought out the writing urge in me again, but this time in a different form. A book of short stories has given me the idea to try writing for this medium. Besides in book form, short stories are always needed for magazines – so now

116

I must study all my old copies of 'Woman's Own'
to see what type of story is most popular.

   I usually only read the problem pages, although in March Biddy had recommended that I read an article in *Woman's Own* called 'The Way to Healthy Womanhood'. I don't think it would have been about eating lots of fruit and veg and walking to school instead of getting the bus. In those long ago days 'healthy womanhood' meant sex education. I don't know how helpful this was to me. I say, very limply for a would-be writer, that the article was 'quite good'.
   I was more interested in proper teenage magazines. On 11 April I wrote:

I bought the new teenage magazine 'Honey'. Back home I spent one and a half hours reading it solidly. By the way, I disagree entirely with what the writer of the article 'CONFIDENCE' has to say. I don't think trying to be a writer will ruin my self confidence. <u>I am not going to say to myself that it isn't important. IT IS! I'M GOING TO TRY AND TRY AND TRY UNTIL I GET SOMEWHERE</u>.

I knew perfectly well that I wasn't ready to write for publication. I *did* enter the *Daily Mirror* Children's Literary Competition in 1960, sending off my entry with fervent wishes and prayers. Jill at school entered too. I didn't win, I wasn't a runner-up, I didn't come anywhere – though I did receive a note saying, *This is to certify that the attached entry reached the final stages of selection.* I was pleased for Jill, if a little jealous, when she received a *Highly Commended* certificate.

Jill was the only girl I knew who loved writing too. She kept a fictional diary about two sisters called Doffles and Bluebell and let a little group of us read the latest entries. She was happy to share it with us, even letting me contribute an entry or two.

I was still writing just for myself, taking it terribly seriously. I worked pretty hard in English lessons at school, trying to please Miss Pierce. I wrote: 'I love Art, but English is still my first love. Not English Grammar, of course, that's foul, but English Essay is heavenly.'

Miss Pierce was an inspirational teacher with a passion for English that was infectious. She had us ordinary, not especially academic fourteen-year-olds reading *Jane Eyre* and *Pride and Prejudice* with joy and enthusiasm, discussing the merits of Rochester and Darcy as eagerly as if they were Elvis or Adam Faith.

118

She was very exacting when it came to the art of writing. She said that an English essay should be like a perfect string of pearls, each paragraph leading on to the next and the next and next until it doubled neatly back to the very beginning.

'What's she *on* about?' Chris mouthed.

I raised my eyebrows and shrugged my shoulders, just to be companionable, but *I* knew. I understood Miss Pierce's lesson on metaphors and similes too. She quoted 'a squirrel sat on the lawn like a coffee pot' – and I *saw* that squirrel and the perfect spout of its paws and handle of its tail. It was like discovering a glorious new game.

I wasn't very good at it at first. Miss Pierce told us to form pairs and describe each other, using metaphors and similes. I squinted long and hard at Chris, gazing into her eyes until we both got the giggles. Her eyes are pale blue – and I couldn't find an original simile to save my life. As blue as the early morning sky? Oh please! As blue as sapphires? How many times has that been used? I ended up with some appalling suggestion about paint water! I'd thought about the first time you swizzle a paintbrush thick with cobalt blue into a clean jug of water and make delicate swirls of pale blue. Chris thought I meant that awful grey sludge colour your paint water becomes after a long painting session and wasn't especially thrilled.

Miss Pierce wasn't either. I tried so very hard with my essays, linking each paragraph together and making my ending fit neatly into my beginning like a clasp, but my essays were nearly always returned with clipped annotations in red pen: 'Too colloquial! Slang! I don't like your tone. This isn't suitable!'

I was always so down-hearted then. I didn't understand that my natural writing style simply wasn't appropriate for a school essay. I'm pretty sure if Miss Pierce were still alive and I gave her one of my books, she'd reach for her red pen after the first paragraph (albeit beautifully linked to the next) and repeat her comments. In fact she'd probably underline them.

However, just occasionally she made my heart leap.

Friday 4 March
In English I got 'Very good work indeed. Well done' which raised my writing hopes as Miss P usually gives mouldy remarks.

And on a golden night in June I wrote:

In the evening Mum went to a parents' meeting at

the school to discuss what subjects we are going to take in the G.C.E. Miss Pierce told her that I was very excellent at English and that she personally would think it a crime if I didn't stay on to the 6th form and take A level English Literature!!!! When Mum told me I was so happy I nearly cried. I might be good as a writer after all.

I had the determination. Then on 14 April I became more focused: 'I bought a WONDERFUL little book called 'Teach Yourself to Write' by Kathleen Betterton. It is wonderfully encouraging and has given me absolutely heaps of ideas.'

I still have my copy of that little book now, well thumbed, with the cover in tatters. Kathleen Betterton says:

No book can teach you how to write, much less how to succeed as a writer. It can teach you only how to teach yourself to write: the rest depends on you. Literary success springs from an unusual combination of originality, luck and industry – especially industry.

I was an odd one out, a strange, shy, weird, imaginative girl who seemed to think differently from everyone else. Did that make me original? I was prepared to be ultra industrious. All right, I could hardly bear to open a school textbook and I was pretty hopeless at helping Biddy with the dusting and vacuuming – but I wrote for hour after hour in my notebooks and diaries.

I wasn't so sure about the luck element though. It's the one thing you can't really control. You can do your best to make your own luck, keeping an eye on literary trends and always being one step ahead. You can force yourself to write an artful letter, make a phone call, approach the right person at a publishing party (though it's agony if you're shy like me). But it's still mostly a matter of luck whether you get your manuscript accepted or not, whether it wins awards and races up the best-seller charts.

My biggest best-seller has been *The Story of Tracy Beaker*. It was a reasonably original idea to choose to write a story about a fierce little girl in a children's home, desperate to be fostered. I certainly worked hard at it. There was no problem with Tracy herself. She sprang to life the moment I made up her name. It was as if she'd seized my pen in her own hot little hand, determined to write her story her way, in her own voice.

I needed to check my facts and find out about fostering. This is where the first piece of luck flashed forth. My friend Bryony works for the

Fostering Network and has very successfully fostered children herself. I asked her if she had any pamphlets about the whole procedure. She gave me a handful, including a yellow booklet specially for children called *My Book About Me*. As soon as I opened it and saw: MY NAME IS . . . I AM . . . YEARS . . . MONTHS OLD. MY BIRTHDAY IS ON . . . my heart started thumping. This was the way to write my book. I imagined my fidgety, stroppy Tracy being sat down by an overly earnest social worker and told to start writing her life story in her special book. She'd start messing about almost at once, telling fibs, going off into little flights of fancy. She'd doodle little drawings all over the page too. I knew I wanted those drawings in the published book.

I nervously asked my then editor, David Fickling, if I could have lots of black and white illustrations throughout the text. This was quite unusual in those days and I worried about it being an extra expense.

David just beamed at me. 'An *excellent* idea, Jacky,' he said. 'I tell you what, I think I know exactly the right person.'

That right person was Nick Sharratt, now my dear friend, who has illustrated every one of my books for nearly twenty years now, and provided each one with an imaginative, distinctive, colourful cover. I am sooooo lucky to have Nick as my artistic partner.

I've written around ninety children's books now and people often ask me if I've ever thought of writing for adults. I *did* actually write five dark and depressing crime novels for adults long ago but I'm not the slightest bit tempted to write for adults now. I only ever want to write for children and teenagers.

However, I didn't *always* feel that way. I read Kathleen Betterton's chapter on 'Writing for Children' and felt disheartened. Kathleen states dogmatically that 'the writer for children must not attempt subtlety of character in which good and evil are blended'. That was precisely what I found disappointing in many children's books. The children just didn't seem *real*. She suggests that children like to read fantasy or adventure or school stories. I hadn't especially enjoyed *any* of these genres. I decided the fault lay with me. I'd simply been a very weird child.

I wrote in my diary:

I have been reading Enid Blyton's autobiography again, but this time far more cynically. She doles out advice again and again to would-be writers – yet surely her books are not all that great. If I ever write I won't write for children. I can't understand how Enid Blyton can write all day, yet leave out everything about real life. Her families don't quarrel, her parents don't nag, her teenagers aren't interested in lipstick and boys, her children never listen to dirty stories or wet themselves, and she ignores babies and pregnancy and sex. Surely all these things must have some part in her life. I just don't see how she can go on about little Noddy and the Famous Five, etc., etc.

Coombe County Secondary School for Girls

9
School

I *hated* school. I didn't mind Latchmere, my primary school, but I couldn't bear my five years at Coombe County Secondary School for Girls. I've been back to Coombe quite a few times to give talks to the girls. I've even presented the prizes at the end of term. I've talked about my school days and I've been polite and tactful, because Coombe now is a very different school. It's warm and relaxed and all the girls (and now there are even *boys* in the sixth form) seem cheerful. They get excellent exam results and they're very sensitive to any girl with special needs. They tick every box and get ten out of ten, full marks for a fine school.

Coombe way back in 1960 was a very different sort of school. *All* schools were different then. There were pointless rules, fierce regulations about uniform, a strict standard of behaviour. You were expected to *conform*. I've never been very good at that.

I loathed most of the lessons too. I disliked PE most of all. Every Friday morning I'd wake up and stick my head out from under my eiderdown, straining my ears. What total joy if I heard rain pattering against the window! Friday was double hockey in our yellow shirts and green shorts – '*G-r-e-e-n and yellow, G-r-e-e-n and yellow, oh Mum be quick, I'm going to be sick, just lay me down to die*,' we sang in the changing rooms.

I had no idea how to play hockey. Miss French, the formidable new PE teacher, had told us the rules, but I'd never listened properly. I simply ran when she blew the whistle – *away* from the ball and the likely whacks from everyone else's hockey sticks. Then she'd blow the whistle again and shout, 'Jacqueline Aitken! What are you *playing* at?'

I didn't want to play at anything. If it poured with rain, making the playing fields too muddy, we couldn't have double hockey. We had country dancing instead, and I adored any kind of dancing.

Hockey was the worst torture, but netball was almost as bad, shivering on the court in the middle of winter, our bare legs beetroot red. I couldn't see the ball until it practically knocked my head off. One day it caught the side of my glasses and sent them skew-whiff, so I went around looking lopsided for weeks.

The scariest ball of all was the hard little rounders ball. Miss French became fed up with me lurking way out on the edge of the pitch as a deep fielder. For one terrible term she insisted I man first post at every game. This was a key position. It was vital that you caught the ball to get the batter out. Miss French was such a sadist. She *knew* I couldn't catch the ball to save my life.

'Come on, Jacqueline Aitken, wake up, watch that ball, catch it, catch it, *catch it*!' she screamed.

I dropped it. I dropped it. I dropped it.

The batting girl hared round second post, third post and was home with a rounder before I'd stopped fumbling. Then Miss French would scream some more, and the other girls on my team would yell at me too. I'd stand there, trying to hold my head high, acting like I couldn't care tuppence whether I caught the stupid ball or not – but I'd be trembling, sometimes dangerously near tears.

Then there was gym. For some inexplicable reason we weren't allowed to wear our green shorts and plimsolls in the gymnasium. We had to run round in our bare feet in just our ugly yellow blouses and our grim grey knickers. We were all shapes and sizes – fat, skinny, wobbly, hairy – so this was bad enough. But in those long-ago days none of us yet used tampons when we had our period. We used sanitary towels hooked onto belts – awful pads like nappies, so of course the shape of them showed right through your knickers.

Sometimes if Miss French was in a very good mood you might whisper to her that you had a very heavy period and then she *might* let you wear your shorts, but not always. You *could* get out of showers if you said you had a period, and that was a relief. Who wants to parade around stark naked so that all your enemies can nudge each other and giggle at your sticky-out tummy or your non-existent chest? We huddled under our towels, and Miss French would shout, 'Get those towels *off*, girls, and get in the showers. Don't be so ridiculous!'

Did Miss French whip her cosy tracksuit off and gambol naked in the showers in front of everyone? No, she did not.

Biddy once suggested that if I was frightened of a teacher I should imagine them naked. I was frightened of our Latin teacher, Miss Cambridge. She looked comical standing pink and plumply bare in my mind's eye, but I was still frightened of her in real life – and oh, how I hated Latin. I never got to grips with it. If we'd been taught about ancient Rome as an introduction I might have become interested. If we'd had a simple conversation book it might even have been fun. (When my daughter learned Latin, the first two words she was taught were 'Hello, sailor!' which made all her class collapse laughing, though they all remembered *Salve nauta* for evermore.)

Miss Cambridge went straight into those bewildering grammatical declensions and conjugations, giving us long lists to learn almost every night. Then we started translating a very long text about Hannibal and his elephants crossing the Alps, and that *should* have been interesting too, but as I understood one word in fifty (probably just Hannibal, elephant and Alp!) I never mentally joined them on their journey. I doodled in the margin, I daydreamed, I made up the next part of my story, I thought about the boy on the bus that morning – and then jumped violently when Miss Cambridge yelled, 'Jacqueline Aitken, are you sure you're paying attention? Translate the last four lines!'

Although I hated Latin I rather liked Miss Cambridge, even though I was scared of her. She used to be funny in a highly sarcastic way, and if she was in a mellow mood she didn't mind if we tried to be funny too.

On Monday 18 January I wrote:

In Latin we had 28 vocabs to learn! Not homework, mind you, but just to be done in our spare time! Honestly, isn't it ridiculous? I'm just dying to leave school. Miss C was complaining that we ought to read more literature, and someone said 'How

can *we when you give us all this homework?'*
We, including Miss C, roared with laughter.

But you had to judge her mood very carefully.
She could squash you flat if she wanted. She had
the ability to march into the rowdiest classroom in
her sensible polished shoes and get instant
respectful silence. She didn't shout or clap her
hands, she just *looked* – and every girl shut her
mouth and sat up straight.

The only way we could get the better of Miss
Cambridge was to sigh and say, 'I wish I knew what
the Colosseum really looked like,' and then Miss
Cambridge would be *off*, telling us about her many
holidays in Rome. Her eyes went dreamy and her
cheeks would flush as she talked, sitting on the
edge of her teacher's table, her large legs planted
on the desk in front, talking away half the lesson
while we sat back happily in our seats. Maybe we
weren't getting the better of her at all: she was
probably as bored with the lesson as we were and
was happy to stride back down Memory Lane to
all those carefree Italian summers.

I hated maths too, but again I liked Miss
Rashbrook. She wasn't fierce like Miss Cambridge,
she was sweet and softly spoken with curly red hair.
She was very pretty, though she was disfigured with

a hunchback. This made her look lopsided and she walked with a little limp. With unusual delicacy we never once referred to this, even amongst ourselves, and anyone imitating her would have been ostracized.

However, we could be hateful to some of the teachers. There was poor Mrs T, who couldn't keep control at all: 'Every time Mrs T turned her back for us to write on the blackboard we slung dishcloths at each other. Soon five or six dishcloths were in orbit!'

We thought we were so funny. I expect she wanted to stuff the dishcloths down our stupid throats.

I did enjoy *some* lessons though. I was always happy in history lessons, especially with a new teacher.

Thursday 7 January
We had Mr Stokes for History for the first time today. He's quite nice but a bit Welsh, look you. He's young, but already he's going a bit bald. I sit next to Jill right in the front. She can be ever so funny. For instance she put on a gruff voice and proceeded to relate to me how she hated Parliament, and was a strong Charles supporter, and how she wanted to throw a brick through the window of 10 Downing

Street at the Mackintosh person. I couldn't help laughing at the 'Mackintosh' and Mr Stokes looked at us two and grinned.

I loved art. I struggled to make my line drawings as delicate and beautiful as Mr Jeziewski's. He had the knack of pressing firmly at the point of a leaf, the turn of an elbow, the corner of a table, that made everything look three-dimensional. I struggled with shading. Sometimes my drawings worked, sometimes they didn't.

We were occasionally taken on sketching parties, which were great fun, but not necessarily productive: 'This afternoon we went sketching to Hampton Court. I drew the ducks most of the time on the pond – I think they're sweet.'

I could have been sketching those fantastic twisty Tudor chimneys, the sculptured yew trees, the gnarled Great Vine, the white classical statues, the fountains, the knot garden ... and I drew the *ducks*!

I drew a lot at home too, making up my own imaginary people, drawing them in a long line, sometimes muttering to them as I coloured them in. No wonder Biddy sighed over me.

I loved English lessons the most of course, though I could be scathing at times:

Then we had English in which we read a babyish play. I wish we could do a really <u>modern</u> play like 'A Taste of Honey', 'The Grass Is Greener', etc., etc. Even Shakespeare would be better. Last term all our group went to see 'As You Like It'. I enjoyed it very much. I also enjoyed the train ride going home when we poked a comb into the adjoining carriage in which there was a highly amused boy.

Now what would I call *that* behaviour? *Babyish!* And how irritating of me not to write more about the play and who was playing Rosalind. It was heroic of Miss Pierce and her colleagues to shepherd us silly giggly girls up to London to the Old Vic. We sat right up in the gods in four-shilling seats, which were really just like big wooden steps. Your back ached unbearably and your bottom got pins and needles, and if you were short-sighted like me the little figures down on the stage were just a blur. But in spite of all this we found those performances thrilling. I was lucky enough to see the young Judi Dench playing Juliet, and that time going home on the train we didn't play silly games with combs and boys, we discussed her brilliant, passionate performance and tried to talk in the same soft sexy voice.

Miss Pierce didn't just take us to plays – she had us perform them too. She ran a drama club on Monday nights. Anyone could join. She chose plays with very large casts to make sure everyone could have a part. They weren't all speaking parts of course.

I secretly hoped I'd get chosen for a main part. I loved English and I was good at reading aloud, but I don't think Miss Pierce thought I was extrovert enough to rise to the occasion. I was always Village Girl or Courtier or Extra Child. It wasn't too taxing standing about on stage, laughing or gasping as required. We generally had a little dance too, and at least we could wear stage make-up and a proper costume.

Monday 11 January
After school I went to Drama Club. At Easter we are going to do a Chinese play, and I saw my costume material today. It is a nice silky pink, far better than my last costume which I had to make out of old brown curtains. But actually the brown didn't look too bad as I wore a lime-green sash and ribbon so it brightened it up.

We rehearsed every Monday evening, but as Easter drew nearer we needed to make more time.

Wednesday 16 March
After school I had to stay for 45 minutes for a Drama
rehearsal. Honestly, Miss Pierce is the limit, she
had told us that we would only need to stay for 10
minutes. The play is coming on slowly but surely.
We have a lovely silver cage and a stuffed
nightingale as props. For the nightingale's voice
Geraldine Taylor blows (behind stage) a sort of
whistle filled with water. It sounds beautiful.

The two performances of *The Imperial
Nightingale* took place on 5 and 6 April.

Tuesday 5 April
THE PLAY!
All the drama club were let off the last lesson so
they could get home, have their tea, and get back to
school in time. I got off at Norbiton with Cherry
and went home. Mum (she's got a stinking cold)
got me some scrambled egg on toast, some tomatoes
and some currant slices, and then after a good wash
I was ready. I cut through the back of our flats and
down Crescent Road and called for Cherry. Her
house is very untidy but has a nice lived-in feeling,
and I like the way that even if she's in on her own
there's always the television blaring, the budgie

cheeping, and the cat providing company as well as noisy miaows. She got ready quickly although she was very nervous as she had quite a big part, and then we set off, two little girls neat and tidy in grey uniform. On the way we met Mrs Eldridge and saw Roger Foulds twice. On the bus we met Mary Todd and Susan Wooldridge. We enabled them to smuggle Miss Pierce's fifteen-shilling bouquet into school without her seeing it. Then we went upstairs and got dressed in our costumes. I wore my pink oriental dress and my pink Alice band with a pink flower on each side. (I was told I looked pretty.) Then we were made up. It was fascinating watching ordinary schoolgirl faces turn into startling Chinese courtiers or suspicious old men, etc. Actually the play didn't go as well as we thought it would, and quite a few girls forgot their lines. But it didn't matter so much today, so long as we are okay tomorrow when the Mayor etc. and the 'Surrey Comet' come.

Wednesday 6 April
It is all over. We have performed our play, and, thank God, it went _beautifully_. During the afternoon Miss P called the Drama Club together and tactfully told us what went wrong yesterday, and told us how to put it right. Mrs Eldridge gave us a lift to school at six o'clock, and Cherry and I dressed and made

up. I made Cherry say her lines to me, because last night she forgot them and said, 'I'm so sorry, I seem to have lost my memory,' getting, incidentally, the biggest laugh of the evening. Miss P took tons of photos of us, including one when the ladies are kneeling down in the spotlight. Anyway, the play really went down <u>well</u>. The audience was very good and laughed at all the jokes Everyone said it was extremely well done, and that the acting, costumes, scenery and properties were all <u>very</u> good.

The day after we were allowed to take it easy.

Thursday 7 April
It is History. As there is only one more day left of the term we have been left to get on with whatever we like. We are all lying sprawled at our desks as we have just had a very strenuous game of Netball, and I, for one, have my blouse sleeves rolled up. It is peaceful in here, except for our low (well, perhaps not!) chatter. Oh! The class below us have just started their rather loud singing. Mr Stokes (not a music lover in spite of his Welsh blood) gives us a look both cynical and ironical. Jill sitting next to me is writing a melodramatic love story. I have just looked up to find Mr Stokes' eyes peering into mine.

He gets up and starts pacing round. He's coming towards me! Help! I must cover this up! Phew – ! He's gone past. Oh no! He's just chalked the word 'Homework' on the board! We gasp in agony. He gives us another of his smiles. I think he's only joking, cross fingers.

I so *hated* homework. It seemed such a terrible waste of time. I could struggle all evening with my maths – even risking Harry's wrath by asking him to help me – but it didn't help me understand how to do it. I could mutter Latin vocabulary over and over and over again, but I was so bored by grim repetition that I couldn't remember a word the next day. I muddled through biology and science and geography and French, sighing and moaning. I tried hard with my English essay homework, though of course I worked *much* harder on my own private writing. At least we didn't get homework for our form lessons, singing, music and PE. Oh God, imagine PE homework!

We tormented little Miss St John in singing, a minute lady who drove to school in an equally minute bubble car: 'For singing we had Miss St John. Everyone ragged her and sang out of tune. I felt rather sorry for her as it must be awful for her to lose control completely.'

Poor Miss St John had such courage. She played the cello, a very large instrument for such a small woman.

Friday 18 March
Honestly, in assembly this morning Miss St John played her cello. *She was so sweet and little behind it, and oh she played so terribly. The notes were all little and queer like she is, and her high notes were about four notes below the right one. I could hardly control my hysterical giggles and at first there reigned a strained silence in the hall except for the fumbly little cello noises. Then one girl gave an awful snort, and that started us off. There was a bellow of six hundred suppressed giggles, all turned into coughs. I had to bite hard on my fingers to stop myself laughing. I couldn't look to my right as Chris was going red in the face suppressing herself, while Sue on my left was openly sniggering. Even Miss Haslett had to laugh, so she bent her head and pretended to be praying!*

Miss Kingston took us for our actual music lesson, and she was a very different type of teacher. No wonder she was snappy with us. We were not a musical bunch, many of us barely progressing

141

beyond the first book of recorder music. We all tooted away valiantly until the spit dribbled disgustingly out of the end of our recorders but we rarely made melodic progress. I remember trying to play Handel's 'Water Music' and all of us collectively drowning in a sea of squawks.

Miss Kingston made us listen to crackly old gramophone records of real musicians playing Handel, Bach and Beethoven. I rather liked this part of the lesson, especially when the music seemed to tell a story. I loved Beethoven's Pastoral Symphony, but tried hard to hide my enthusiasm. If you sat with too rapt an expression, everyone would laugh and tease you and label you a swot. It wasn't cool to like classical music, though we all adored dancing to a record called *Asia Minor* which was a jazzed-up version of Grieg's Piano Concerto.

Sometimes the records seemed to go on for ever. It could get very boring just sitting there, so we worked out ways of communicating with each other. We didn't dare whisper in front of Miss Kingston. Passing notes was decidedly risky. Chris and I had learned the rudiments of sign language for the deaf from a schoolgirl diary and this proved useful during protracted school assemblies, but Miss Kingston was on to us the minute we tried it in music.

Wednesday 27 January
Chris, Lyn and I were doing deaf and dumb
alphabet in music, and Miss Kingston saw us. At
the end of the record she asked (or rather shouted!)
what had we been doing. We sat silent. 'Answer me
at once!' We still sat silent. 'The girl on the end'
(me) 'you tell me!' Silence. 'At once!' 'Well, er, you
see,' I said, trying in vain to think of some excuse,
'Christine was, er, playing with her fingers.' The
whole group roared with laughter and we three got
a severe telling off.

I didn't mean to tell tales on poor Chris, I just
blurted out the first thing that came into my head
– but she wasn't best pleased with me. She still
sometimes teases me about it now, hundreds of
years later.

I hated the whole *atmosphere* of school. My heart
would sink as I trudged up the path and went
through the glass doors into the cloakrooms. There
was always a fug of damp grey gabardines and old
shoes as soon as you walked in. As the day
progressed the smells got worse. Our school dinners
were made on the premises and in retrospect were
totally delicious:

143

Monday 8 February
We had chips, corned beef and American salad and
mince and apple tart for dinner today, not bad for
school dinners.

Tuesday 9 February
Dinner was steak pie, greens and mashed potato,
and semolina and jam for pud. Pretty awful, n'est-
ce pas?

Wednesday 10 February
After dinner (porky sort of meat, peas, roast potatoes
and caramel pie) Carol, Cherry and I went up to
the library to do homework.

Cherry was the dinner monitor on our school
dinner table that year. If everyone had finished
their platefuls the dinner monitor could put up her
hand, and when the supervising teacher had given
her permission she could charge up to the kitchen
counter and ask for seconds. We might moan about
our school dinners but *some* seconds were definitely
worth having. Mrs Legge, our school cook, made
delicious fish and chips on Fridays, and her pastry
was total perfection. She made beautiful steak and
kidney pies; her fruit pies – apple, apricot and plum
– were glorious; and her occasional-for-a-special-

144

treat lemon meringue pies always made my mouth water. So we obeyed Cherry as she urged us to bolt our food down in five minutes so we would be in with a chance of more. It's a wonder we didn't hiccup our way all through afternoon school.

Mrs Legge worked miracles – imagine baking enough pies for hundreds of girls – but her budget was limited and mince and stewing steak were served up very regularly. I hated both. You started being able to smell them cooking by break time, and by twelve o'clock the whole school reeked of this strong savoury smell, appallingly reminiscent of body odour.

The corridors were frequently filled with a horrible burning smell too. Mrs Legge never burned her dinners. This was all the fault of the incinerator in the girls' toilets. We all used sanitary towels and in those days they weren't properly disposable. If you had your period you were supposed to go in the special end toilet, which had an incinerator – but it was a tricky customer and if you didn't insert your disgusting towel just so, it would spitefully send out smelly smoke. Everyone would look at you and point when you came out of the toilet.

We all smelled too, in various ways. The girls smelled of bubble gum and hairspray and nail varnish and Goya's Entice scent and fresh tangy sweat. The teachers smelled of chalk and talcum powder and Polo mints. The men smelled of tobacco, and the French master reeked of unwashed body. We hated having to go up to his desk – and when you stood there breathing shallowly he'd often slyly pat your breast or bottom.

Some brave girls in another form went to Miss Haslett and complained about this teacher's wandering hands and suggestive remarks. Miss Haslett told the girls they were making disgusting allegations because they had warped minds and sent them away in disgrace.

I was only in really serious trouble once in my five years at Coombe. It was a sporty school and Miss French and her colleague Miss Snelling were proud of the hockey and netball teams. They were particularly keen on athletics and our school was entered for the County Championships at Motspur Park.

Chris and Carol and Cherry and Sue and Jill and all my other friends weren't at all interested. They weren't quite such duffers at games as me but they knew they were nowhere near speedy enough to represent the school at athletics. *I* came last in any race, I couldn't do the high or long jump, I was downright dangerous with a discus or javelin in my hand and I couldn't even *lift* the shot, let alone put it anywhere.

I went off in a daydream whenever Miss French talked excitedly about the wretched Motspur Park athletics. She was outlining the arrangements – it seemed the school was hiring coaches so we could all go and watch – as if it was a serious treat.

Miss French told us we had to tell her at the next PE lesson whether we needed a seat on the coach or not so that she could book it.

'Of course, if you don't wish to go you don't have to. It is entirely voluntary,' she said.

Chris nudged me. 'Did you hear that, Jac? What does that mean, exactly?' she whispered.

'It means we don't have to go!' I said happily.

'But we'll get into trouble,' Cherry said. 'You know she *wants* us to go.'

'Yes, but do *you* want to go?'

'Of course not!'

We conferred with all the other girls in the class. *None* of the non-team girls wanted to go. So we decided to tell Miss French politely that we simply didn't wish to attend. She couldn't really object, could she? She'd *said* the trip was voluntary.

Miss French was in a bad mood the next PE lesson.

'Come along, you lazy girls, you're five minutes late already. Change into your kit in double-quick time and then go and sit in the gym. No talking now!'

We got changed quickly without so much as a whisper. We sat cross-legged on the polished wooden floor. Miss French squeaked towards us in her gym shoes. Her whistle bounced on her chest. She clutched a clipboard and pen.

'Right, I need to get this coach business sorted and then we'll get on with our lesson.' She consulted her register. She was going to do us in alphabetical order. Oh God. Guess whose name was right at the top.

'Jacqueline Aitken!' Miss French called. 'Do you want a seat on the coach?'

Her pen was poised, ready to tick me. Everyone was staring at me. I swallowed.

'No, thank you, Miss French,' I said.

Miss French drew in her breath so that the whistle bounced on her bosom. 'Are your parents taking you to Motspur Park in their car?' she asked.

'No, Miss French.'

'So *why* don't you need a seat on the coach?'

'Because I don't want to go, thank you,' I mumbled.

'You don't want to *goooo*?'

Oh God oh God oh God.

'No, Miss French,' I said in a squeak.

'Well, that's just *typical* of you, Jacqueline Aitken! It isn't enough that you're a disgrace in

148

every single PE class. You never even *try* to catch a ball and you won't run to save your life. You're bone idle and lazy. But what about all your friends and colleagues? How can you be so selfish? Don't you *care* about all the girls competing? Don't you *want* Coombe to win?'

I couldn't care less, but I could see a truthful response wouldn't be wise.

'I've got used to you being useless in my classes, never trying hard, never taking PE seriously, but I thought at the very least you cared about all the other girls. I even thought you might have just a little loyalty to *me*.'

I stared back at her, wondering how she could seriously think this.

'Take that expression off your face, you insolent girl. I'm sick of the sight of you. You'll never amount to anything, do you hear me? Do you know why? You've no team spirit. You don't care about anyone else. Well, believe you me, no one will ever care about you. Very well, *don't* come to Motspur Park to support your team. Now, who's next?' she said, consulting the register again.

I went to sit down.

'No, you stay standing, Jacqueline Aitken. You'll stand there till the end of the lesson.' She frowned at the register. 'Jill Anderson. Do *you* need a place on the coach?'

149

Jill said yes. I didn't blame her. I'd have said yes too if I'd been second on the register. Everyone said yes. I was stuck standing there, the girl who'd said no.

I held my head high and clenched my fists, telling myself I didn't care. But my heart was banging *boom-boom-boom* inside my chest and I knew I was trembling. It all seemed a ridiculous fuss about nothing and blatantly unfair as she'd said attendance at Motspur Park was voluntary. As if it made any difference to anyone whether I was there or not. She kept glancing in my direction, acting as if I'd deliberately tried to poison the entire athletics team.

I didn't really believe her remarks about never amounting to anything – and to be fair, I don't think she really meant it. She was just furious, worried that all the other girls would follow my example and she'd be left looking a fool without any girls cheering on her wretched team.

She was right about one thing though. I don't think I *do* have any team spirit. I never identified with school. I never felt proud of my uniform. I never sniffled when we sang the school hymn at the end of term. I never cheered with genuine enthusiasm. I loved my special friends, I liked some of the teachers, but Coombe as an institution meant nothing to me.

Coombe's lovely now. Maybe it was lovely for all the other pupils back in 1960. I was just the odd one out.

A dance class party

10
Dancing

Miss French thought I was the most bone-idle, lazy girl at Coombe. I wasn't at all. I walked to school every day, a good two- or three-mile hike from our flats in Kingston all the way over to New Malden. If I'd spent my week's bus fare on a paperback or Woolworths notebook I'd walk all the way home again too.

Sometimes I walked with Sue next door, sometimes I walked with another Susan, a girl from Kingsnympton, the council estate up the hill. I liked both Sues. I could have a cosy chat with Sue next door about our dancing class and a moan about our mums. I knew the other Sue less well, but she was interesting, telling me all about the feuds and gangs and punch-ups on the Kingsnympton estate. She also passed her *Bunty* comic on to me every week. I considered myself way beyond the *Bunty* stage but it wouldn't have been polite to say so – and I was happy to read anything.

I think I liked the walk to school most, though, when I was on my own. I'd always been a very dreamy girl and yet nowadays there was very little opportunity to dream. I was supposed to stay on red alert, listening and concentrating at school, and then in the evenings I had to struggle through my homework before rushing out to go dancing or to the pictures.

But if I walked to school on my own I could daydream for nearly an hour as I marched along in my Clarks clodhoppers, swinging my satchel. Sometimes I made up stories. Sometimes I pretended I was being interviewed by a journalist: 'I'm simply bowled over by your first novel, Jacqueline. I've never encountered such remarkable talent in one so young,' etc., etc.! Sometimes I peered at the houses all around me and imagined the people inside and the lives they were living. The first half of the journey was much the most interesting because I stepped from one world into quite another.

Cumberland House was a small 1950s council estate, three six-storey blocks of flats. It was quite genteel as council estates go. A window would get broken once in a while or someone used the lift as a toilet, but mostly we were a timid, law-abiding tribe, though still relatively poor. Biddy and Harry had only just got a car and a telephone. We still didn't have a washing machine or a fridge and owned just a very small black and white television. We went for a holiday once a year but we hardly ever went out as a family otherwise.

We had the special treat on Sundays of a shared bottle of Tizer and a Wall's family block of raspberry ripple ice cream after our roast chicken. This was High Living as far as we were concerned. The flat was still furnished with the dark utility table and chairs and sideboard bought just after the war, with a gloomy brown sofa and two chairs filling up the rest of the room. We weren't allowed to sit on the sofa because it would disturb Biddy's complicated arrangement of decorative cushions. She sat in one chair, Harry in the other, while I perched on an unpleasant brown leatherette pouffe.

We didn't have a garden to relax in but we *did* have a balcony. Biddy didn't go in for tubs of flowers or window boxes as she said that plants would shed their leaves and make a mess – but she let me have a hammock slung precariously from one end of the balcony to the other. I'd begged for a hammock for my birthday, thinking it would be romantic to swing idly while reading a book, just like all the girls in Victorian storybooks. I hadn't bargained on the fact that swinging, idly or otherwise, made me feel queasy, and if I wasn't cautious enough the hammock would go *clonk* against the side of the concrete balcony and give my hip a nasty bruise.

But once I'd walked out of the flats, crossed the very noisy main road and passed the pub opposite, I stepped into George Road, which could have been on a different planet. It was a private road, part of the Coombe estate, the very poshest part of Kingston where celebrities lived in enormous houses and played on the exclusive golf course. I wasn't so keen on the modern houses, palatial though they were. I liked the enormous Victorian houses, some now turned into private schools. I'd imagine myself back in time, living there, the bookish daughter of the house, *not* the grubby scullery maid.

Then I'd turn down a smaller road and reach my favourite house. I describe it in a June entry in my diary:

Down the Drive there are some absolutely beautiful houses with enormous gardens – my favourite has a great big pond, almost a lake, with willows all around and a little waterfall leading onto a much smaller pool surrounded by bluebells. There is a fence and hedge all round so you can only see bits at a time. At the moment their rhododendron bushes are all in bloom, a lovely crimson.

I found out that this beautiful house, Kingfishers, had once been part of the John Galsworthy estate. I didn't read his Forsyte Saga books until they were serialized on television in the late sixties. It was enough just knowing that the house had once been owned by a *writer*.

I wrote a lamentably bad poem about the house:

KINGFISHERS
I peer through the bamboo leaves;
No privet hedges here.
The sweet pea on the trellis weaves;
Bees, satisfied, appear.

The gabled house stands proudly
Embraced by tender creeper.
Only a chaffinch, singing loudly,
Ignoring me, the peeper.

Small curious paths brazenly wind
Beneath the silver birches,
Scattered round, to the garden's rind.
Peace here, as in churches.

A feathery aged willow protects
The quiet unruffled lake.
A tiny woodsy island injects

Itself, obstinately opaque.

The water trickles, filters through
To a secret mossy pond,
Springtimely fringed by bells of blue
And the fern's lacy frond.

Oh house, generations-long secure
With your cosy ingle-nooks.
Your magic easily did procure
John Galsworthy and his books.

Would that I might live here too,
Free from cares and danger;
So easy, Jeevesy. Troubles few;
But I am just a stranger.

As I trudged on through the less exciting suburban streets of New Malden I'd daydream about being a famous best-selling author one day – and maybe *I'd* live in a house like Kingfishers.

Dream on, little Jacky Daydream! I live in a beautiful house now and I wouldn't want to swap it with anyone, but my lovely home looks like a little cottage compared to Kingfishers.

I was clearly exercising my imagination as well as my legs as I walked to school. I also went dancing at least twice a week, sometimes more. Not *ballet* dancing, though I'd have loved to learn. When I was little I longed to wear a neat black practice dress, a pink angora bolero and pale pink ballet shoes like some of the girls at my primary school. Biddy thought ballet a waste of time and didn't want to get lumbered with making my costumes.

She sent me to old-time dancing classes instead, mainly because they were held just down the road on a Saturday morning and I could go with Sue. There were fourteen or so other pupils, all girls. We paired up, and because I was a little taller than Sue I had to be the boy. I'm *still* better at being the boy at dancing and have to fight not to take the lead and steer my partner around the floor!

We didn't have to wear special outfits like ballet dancers. We didn't even have to wear special shoes, though lots of the girls wore silver or sparkly strappy dance sandals. I longed to have a pair, but had to make do with boring black patent. Perhaps that's why nowadays I have such a weakness for silver or sparkly shoes!

Sue and I went dancing together for years. I started to feel I was getting too old for it – and we weren't really progressing. We'd got our bronze and silver and gold medals but we were never going to be real competition standard. I skipped dancing class the first two Saturdays in January, but on the sixteenth I wrote:

For once I went Old Time dancing with Sue. I quite enjoyed myself although I prefer Friday night dancing. [Of course I did – it was ballroom, and there were boys]. *I wasn't the oldest for once because Sandra came* [the girl who lent me *Peyton Place*]. *We danced the Quadrilles and it was ever such good fun. Also we did the Maxina which I enjoy doing as it is so unusual.*

I can't for the life of me remember how to do the quadrilles or the maxina now. I can vaguely remember old-time favourites like the valeta and the Boston two-step, and I still get tempted to whirl about the room whenever I hear a Viennese waltz – my feet go forward-side-together-back-behind-front of their own accord.

Mr Crichton, the old-time teacher, threw a party for all his dancing students at the end of January.

It was very good fun and I had a lovely time, but not as good as last Saturday! [I'd been to a party. I'll be writing about it later in a chapter on boys.]

We had some good novelty dances and some ballet shows that Sandra was in. Then all these lifeboat men in raincoats and sou'westers came in through the door pulling a rope and singing 'Yo heave ho'. Then into the hall on the end of the rope was pulled a man on a potty reading a newspaper. Everyone was so amazed they just stood open-mouthed. Guess what! Sue and I won the Maxina competition and got a lovely gold medal each!

I wore this gold medal the next Saturday when I went dancing.

We did a good square dance called the Caledonians. Next week we are all taking sandwiches and staying on in the afternoon to train for the Kingston dancing competition to be held at the Coronation Hall.

The following Saturday

We did the Quadrilles; I love the music to that. We had a picnic lunch there, and then had another hour's dancing, this time competition work. We had some exercises to do, and next week we've got to bring

161

old sheets to put on the ground as we're going to do exercises on the ground. It's going to be jolly indecent raising stockinged legs in front of Mr Crichton!

Saturday 20 February
Went dancing. We learnt some new dances, but not very nice ones. When it was time for the Beginners to go home and for us to have our picnic lunches this gorgeous boy and an enormous Afghan hound came and collected one of the little girls. Naturally, I went up and stroked the hound, then stared up into the boy's face and smiled. Am impatiently waiting for next week to come. We had a good chat eating our lunch in the cloakroom gathered round the oil stove on old benches. Sandra, who is 15 in July so nearest in age to me, told us she had three brothers. 'How old?' came a chorus. 'All younger than me,' Sandra replied. 'Ooh!' came disappointedly from the chorus. Afterwards we had to do some horrible exercises lying on the floor. We all had terrible giggles!

Saturday 27 February
When I woke up I thought it was Friday like I do every Saturday and tried to force myself out of my lovely warm nest. Then the gorgeous realisation swept over me and I was able to go back to sleep.

I went dancing. Sandra, Christine, Wendy, Sue and I had a good chat. The dog turned up again to collect the little girl but with a middle-aged man instead of its other owner. Honestly, the exercises were so funny. Doing bicycles was bad enough, but when we had to lie on our tummies and just balance on our hands and the tips of our toes, and also when we had to raise both our chest and our legs off the floor so that we were curved, and only lying on our waists; well, we were just prostrate with giggles. Sandra told me that her hair was not naturally curly. I was amazed as it looks so pretty. I must try putting mine up in rollers. Also she said she goes to a co-ed school, and learns typing as well as ordinary lessons. Isn't she lucky!

Saturday 5 March
Lay in, and then got dressed in white jumper and pink and mauve mohair skirt and went dancing. We learnt a new square dance called the Tango Quadrilles. Now we know four: the Quadrilles, the Lancers, the Caledonians and now the Tango Quadrilles. The middle-aged man turned up with the dog again. Sue didn't stay the third hour. She might have let me know beforehand. After we'd eaten our picnic lunches we chattered a while, and then really slogged away at the Filed Waltz, Valeta,

Latchford and the Military Two Step. The competition is in a month's time! Mr C was giving us all butterflies when he told us about the strict rules. As Sue wasn't there I had to dance with Mr C. Honestly, such a fuss about a little thing like a salute. Mr C had us all in front of him, and finally we could do it as 'snappy' as he wished. My poor arm aches now.

Saturday 12 March
I went dancing with Sue this morning. Sandra has had her hair cut, it looks nice, but I preferred it long and curly, it made her look more pretty. We had our picnics and then slogged for another hour at the Lola Tango, Fyle, and the Premia. Ga and Gongon said they would like to come and watch me at the competition on 2 April. I cannot think of an excuse to prevent them coming without making them feel hurt, but I shall be very embarrassed, especially if I am knocked out the first round. (It sounds like boxing!)

Saturday 26 March
I dressed in my new sprigged violet cotton skirt, and Mum's mauve Spring coat and went to Kingston with Carol and Cherry. Then I went dancing. We slogged and slogged (the competition is next week) and then Mr C played my new record

on his record player for me. At our picnic lunch Sue and I talked to Sandra a lot. Then another hour of <u>slogging</u> – and it was time to go home.

The competition was on 2 April. After all that build-up I wrote precisely two lines about it: 'In the afternoon went to the Comp. but Sue and I didn't get anywhere.'

It had been a total nightmare. There were lots of girls who danced together, but they all had specially made matching net costumes in excitingly violent colours: purple, crimson, shocking pink, with matching sequinned bodices.

Our mums didn't do dressmaking. My grandma used to sew beautifully but now her arthritis was so bad she couldn't tackle elaborate dance costumes. We wore our mums' party dresses, which were vaguely similar blue florals. We looked ridiculous with these big matronly dresses hanging off our puny shoulders. Our hair wasn't styled in a chignon, our faces weren't made up, and we didn't have the right shoes. We did our best, dancing with fixed smiles and desperate eyes – and we were eliminated in the first round.

Friday night ballroom dancing was much more fun. We didn't take the dancing part too seriously – and there were boys. Not many boys. None of my crowd went with a boy – but we were in the same *room* with them, and occasionally changed partners and danced with them, solemnly waltzing or quickstepping up and down the ballroom (a long bleak hall in Surbiton where Sainsbury's now stands).

Friday 8 January
A whole crowd from Coombe went dancing – Carol, Sue, Jill, Cherry, Judith and I. Carl (Mr Bryant) taught us thank goodness. I can't bear that awful Len that sometimes teaches us, when he dances with you he breathes a whole barful of beer over you. Peter and the other reasonable boys weren't there but dear Laura and co. were. She's very common [oh God, I sound like Biddy!], but I like her hair when she doesn't scrape it into a French roll. It is a sort of long pageboy. I think I'll grow my hair and have it like that; that is if it will go into a pageboy.

Laura was Peter's girlfriend. He was the only decent boy at dancing. We all raised our eyebrows and shook our heads over her short skirts and high heels – but we secretly envied her like anything.

Friday 15 January
In the evening I went dancing with Carol and Jill.
Peter wasn't there again, and neither was dear
Laura etc. this time. I've come to my own
conclusions about those two. Carl wasn't there
so that Len character took us, but it was quite
good fun actually. It was great fun walking
home through the snow singing at the tops of
our voices.

We didn't go dancing the next Friday: this
was when we all flocked to the cinema to see
Expresso Bongo.

Friday 29 January
Sue came dancing with us this evening. Carl took
us thank goodness. No Peter again, he hasn't come
for ages. Not that I care, now I've got Ken. Laura
and Veronica turned up in tight skirts above their
knees. Sue's eyebrows went up when she saw them!
I might wear my straight skirt to dancing, my
blue one.

Ken was a boy I'd just met. There'll be more
about him later. Lots more.

Friday 12 February
In the evening I went dancing. Sue didn't come, or Judith, but Carol and Jill did. I wore my new nail varnish and new flatties which were lovely for dancing in. We did a lot of complicated Samba steps and I had Peter for a partner. After Ken I think he's terribly ordinary. He's taking his silver medal next week. Jill asked him if he had enjoyed 'Expresso Bongo' and he said he had. Peter forsook Laura and accompanied Anne home this week. She looks about sixteen, wears sloppy jumpers, very tight skirts and crimson nail varnish.

Friday 19 February
I went dancing with Carol. We made friends with a Tiffins girl and she told us the amazing news that Anne (see last Friday) is only in the first year at Tiffs!!!

Friday 26 February
Jill, Carol and I went dancing. I asked Peter whether he had taken his silver medal yet, but he said he was taking it next week. We did some funny new cha cha steps and some new rhythm dancing.

Friday 4 March
After school Carol, Jill (in a new tartan skirt) and I went dancing. Laura came, but Peter didn't, so

that was one in the eye for her. She is really common, but some of the things she says are very funny. When Len was trying to be funny, she said, bored, 'What a queer old man.' Carl knows my name! He called me Jacqueline!

Friday 11 March
Sue came dancing with Carol and I. None of the girls seem to like Carl, but I think he is sweet. He's certainly 'all there'. Going home Carol said my mother sounded a pushing type. The bitch! I don't care what she says about me, or even my friends (e.g. Chris and Jill) but I will not have her saying things like that about my mother.

I wonder what she *said* exactly. I don't know why I got in such a state. I loved Biddy very much but I couldn't possibly deny that she *was* pushy. She called this having *gump* – short for gumption – and lamented the fact that I possessed no gump whatsoever.

Friday 1 April
As I was standing at the bus stop ready to go dancing I turned towards the flats and waved at Mummy. Guess who was standing at the next door window.

Jeremy! He must have thought I was waving at him!
A new boy actually turned up at dancing, but not
anything particular. Peter did not come and neither
did Laura. We did the quickstep again. I could do
it when I danced with Carl and with other girls who
could do it, but not when I did it with someone who
couldn't do it, as I was a girl and could not take
the lead. On the way home I bought a red fat shilling
exercise book for my new story. It is coming along
nicely at the moment, thank you.

Friday 8 April
Jill, Carol and I went dancing. I wore a summer
dress for the first time. We did a new dance that
was good fun. Jill, Carol and I had to show the
others how to do it.

There was no dancing over Easter, and when we
went back it didn't seem so beguiling. I didn't
bother to write about it for several weeks, then:

Friday 27 May
After school I didn't go dancing as I'm getting a
bit sick of it. So is Carol, so I think we'll start going
to the Lagoon on Fridays instead.

We'd been to the lagoon the day before. It was called Surbiton Lagoon but it was actually in Tolworth, a bus ride away. It was a wonderful white art deco lido with a big open-air pool and a proper diving board. I *wish* it was still there now. I'd spent most of the long sunny summer of 1959 going to the lagoon. It was only sixpence (2Hp) to go in, so Biddy would give me a shilling (5p) each day and that covered my bus fares and a packet of crisps as a treat. We'd stay there all day long, chatting, reading, eyeing up the boys and diving in for a swim whenever we got too hot.

Obviously the lagoon was closed during the winter but it opened up in May.

Thursday 26 May
After school Cherry, Carol and I went to the Lagoon. It was SMASHING. We certainly picked the right day for going, as it was lovely and warm. It was cold at first in the water, but after a minute or two it was delicious. We all brought our teas so we could stay in till gone seven, when the session ended. We all wore our glamorous swimming costumes and painted our toenails.

But it didn't stay warm. Carol and I went to the lagoon at half-term.

171

Tuesday 7 June
In the morning Carol and I optimistically went to
Surbiton Lagoon. It was f-r-e-e-z-i-n-g, and when we
eventually plucked up courage to jump in the water
we were very nearly frozen solid. I was surprised
that there weren't any icebergs floating around.
Anyway, when it began to pour with rain it was just
the limit, and C and I packed up and ran for the
warmth of the changing rooms. After we were warm
and dry and changed we decided to go. As we were
standing at the bus stop guzzling our packed lunches
my front tooth filling came out again, blast it.

Oh, that front tooth! It was the bane of my life, always falling out at awkward moments. Long ago, when I'd first learned to swim at the age of six, I'd bashed my mouth against the stone side of the swimming pool as I struggled to get out. Both my front teeth were chipped, and when I reached my teens my dentist sent me up to the Royal Dental Hospital in Leicester Square to see if they could fix me up with a rudimentary crown. If anything went wrong I had to trail all the way up to London. So the next day:

In the morning I went up to the Royal Hospital of

Dentists and had my tooth seen to. This time I didn't have Mr Arnold but a fat chubby student who reminded me of a teddy bear. He was very nice though, and I could have hugged him when he asked if I went out to work yet!

I'm rather impressed that at fourteen I was able to make that journey on the train up to Waterloo and then take the tube to Leicester Square. I was always supposed to come straight back after my dental treatment but I didn't always, especially if it was a school day and I could miss maths and PE. I'd sit on a bench in Leicester Square and read my book, hoping that everyone would think me a young secretary on my lunch break. I didn't have enough money on me to buy myself lunch but I'd look longingly at the menu in the window of the Golden Egg restaurant. Then, to distract myself from my hunger pangs, I'd wander along to the Charing Cross Road and peer even more wistfully in the windows of the second-hand bookshops.

11

Boys Boys Boys

Oh dear. This is the hardest chapter to write. I was so *silly*.

Chris asked me if I'd like to start going with her to the Youth Fellowship group at her local Methodist church. I wasn't a Methodist, I wasn't any kind of church-goer , but Chris said there were sometimes interesting discussions – and lots of boys went. So on Sunday 3 January I ate my Sunday roast chicken hurriedly, got myself dressed up (the eau-de-nil outfit) and caught the bus over to New Malden.

The Youth Fellowship discussion group was run by a gentle bald man called Mr Golden, who welcomed me warmly.

Mr Golden based his talk on stars, and told us about horoscopes etc. Afterwards I had to give my name and address to Michael Young to be put on the register. Chris pipes up 'Why not give him your vital statistics as well?' and M.Y. and I promptly blush scarlet. When we got outside the Church we saw

175

Johnny Wilkins smoking a pipe! I couldn't believe my eyes as he is only about sixteen. He looked so funny, puffing away self consciously. We now call him Sherlock Holmes amongst ourselves.

I settled into going to Youth Fellowship every Sunday. I don't think I ever contributed to any discussion. I was far too shy, though I was Miss Gabby Gossip with Chris.

Sunday 17 January
Before the service everyone natters away to each other, and Chris and I were engrossed in conversation. We suddenly realised that Viv was nudging us and that everyone was staring at us. Poor Mr Golden had been trying to begin the service and had said 'Shall we commence by singing . . .' whereupon Chris had said (in reply to me) 'No!' Everybody burst out laughing and a boy called out 'Big Brother has his eye on you.'

The next day I wrote:

When I got home after Y.F. Mum asked me which

boy I liked best. Little does she know it's John Wilkins! At school Sue told Chris I liked him but Chris has sworn faithfully not to tell him.

I liked John Wilkins the pipe smoker?! But not for long.

Wednesday 20 January
I can't imagine loving a man, not now. Of course I get crushes on boys, but that's not proper love. In Biology Chris told me that she thought J.W. liked Gloria Hastings. That has rather put me off him.

The next Saturday there was a special Youth Fellowship Tramps Party. I've inked red and blue stars at the top of the page. This was clearly a magical occasion for me, though reading my diary entry now, it sounds so touchingly soppy.

Saturday 23 January
Met Chris in New Malden at 10 o'clock. We went round the shops and bought some loaves and marge for the church 'Tramps Party' in the afternoon. We dropped them off in the Church hall and then went

back to Christine's. After lunch Jan, Val, Chris and I sat at the table doing our homework. At 5.30 Chris and I changed into old slacks and sweaters and then went out and met Carol, Lyndsay, Viv and Rosemary. Then we nervously went into the hall and sat on a table together. We were soon jiving with each other. Then Mr G came and the party began. It was lovely! We played some gorgeous games and it was all such fun! We played a sort of Pass the Parcel only there were forfeits like find the boy who is the most ticklish, or find the girl with the smallest waist. This boy measured mine and said I was 21 inches and I couldn't possibly have been as I am 24–25 inches. There was also a husband and wife game in the dark! But one game you had to sit on the boys' laps. Ken said, 'Oh, this is better,' and put his arms round me! I think he's smashing!!!

I went very eagerly to Youth Fellowship the next day.

Sunday 24 January
Went to Y.F. in the afternoon. Carol went too, and seemed to enjoy herself. I sat next to Michael Young. When we stood up to sing Ronnie put a hymn book

on my chair and I sat down straight on it. Isn't he a beast! Ken said, 'Excuse me, Jacqueline.' Oh well, I'm getting on!

Monday 25 January
Today Chris has done nothing but talk and think of Peter Lock, the boy who she danced with on Sat. and I have done nothing but talk and think of Ken. I think he is wonderful, and very good looking in his own way. He is about 16 or 17 and goes to work. He lives in New Malden. He has a little sister Geraldine who goes to Brownies and his father is a Cub master. Ken has a fair sort of long crew cut and lovely eyes. I gleaned this information from Chris about his age and family etc., the rest I observed. I only wish he had been my husband in the game on Sat. because lots of the others were kissing!

Thursday 28 January
We had another Maths theorem test, worst luck. I still think of Ken an awful lot. Chris has told me that Glenda told her in strictest confidence, mind you, that he smoked a lot. I don't care!

Friday 29 January
Saw Glenda at dinner time and casually mentioned Ken. It was obvious she hates him, but she said he

didn't drink or anything, just smoked. What's wrong with a boy of seventeen or so that smokes?

Sunday 31 January
After roast dinner dashed off to Y.F. It was terribly hot in that little room, and I almost fell asleep, except that I was so intent on trying to screw my head round and look at Ken. We had to discuss some questions Mr Golden gave us. I had to be in that horrible S— boy's group. Ugh, I think he's awful. So overbearing, aggressive, almost fatherly!

Monday 1 February
You'll never ever guess who I saw by Norbiton station. Ken! I almost fell over with surprise! He was riding a bike and wearing blue jeans. I could recognise that fair crew cut anywhere. I don't think he saw me. Next Sunday I'm going to ask him if it was him. I hope he'll tell me where he works. I only hope he hasn't got a girlfriend. I know he used to like Anne Wilkins, Johnny's sister, but I don't think he does any more.

Tuesday 2 February
Saw <u>him</u> again this morning. He looked at me as if he recognised me this time. Next Sunday looms ahead! I have a shocking cold, but I don't feel a bit depressed. I feel very happy, and you can guess why!

Wednesday 3 February
I went down the hill and saw Ken. Oh, you'll never guess where I saw him go! Kingston Hill Motor Works. Bang next door, almost! I'm ever so excited about that!

Thursday 4 February
Saw my Ken again this morning. Sue can't understand what I see in him as he isn't really handsome. I don't know myself what it is, except that I like him so much.

Friday 5 February
Saw <u>him</u> again. It is wonderful being able to see him every day. It makes the day start off right, and puts me in a good mood straight away.

Sunday 7 February
Woke up early this morning. I put the light on, did my hair, and then settled down to homework. Oh how I HATE it. It rules my life, it does really.

In the afternoon went to Y.F. Us girls were the first there (I got a lift in Carol's car) and Mr Golden asked us to put the chairs out. We only put the girls' out. Mr G asked where the boys would sit and Chris said 'On our laps,' whereupon Mr G replied 'A good idea!' Didn't get a chance to talk to Ken as he came late and went early. We talked about newspapers; it was quite interesting. When he stood up to sing Ronnie and John put a hymn book on Brian Tiplady's chair. He sat down, and almost fell off again. It was so funny!

I was so obsessed with Ken that I thought it worth writing in my diary on 9 February: 'Saw Ken but only a glance as I went past him on the bus.' On 10 February I didn't even see him and thought *this* important enough to record: 'Didn't see Ken today, worst luck. Chris and Sue told me to call out hello to him next time I see him. I think I will, you know. I wonder what will happen!'

Nothing much! On 11 February: 'I didn't see Ken <u>again</u> but Chris told me she saw him on her way home from school, the lucky thing.'

I didn't mention him for a day or two, and then:

Sunday 14 February
At Y.F. Mr Golden suggested that we girls should make a cloth for the table. No fear! I'm hopeless at needlework. We talked about adverts this week and it was very interesting. We had to divide up into two groups and think up as many adverts as we could in 10 minutes, like 'Cadum for Madam' and 'Hey diddle diddle there's a hole in the middle'.

We thought of piles including 'Goodnight, sleep tight, and don't forget to use Harpic every night'. Us girls had hysterics when Mr G started talking about 'home helps'. [Why?] Ken dashed off like last week so didn't get a chance to talk to him. But actually my interest is decidedly waning as he is rather scruffy. I'll just have to find someone else.

It didn't take me long.

Wednesday 17 February
Saw CRAIG going home. Oh, I think he is so nice but I mustn't let on to anyone.

Craig? He was a blond boy who lived in our flats. There'll be more about him later. Much more interestingly to me now, that diary entry continues:

Saw Mr Townsend on the 213 bus. I almost fainted! He looked ever so tanned and handsome and talked to Carol and me. Carol agreed with me that Mr Townsend looked very young. I remarked that perhaps it is only because we are older. He said that we were nearly old enough to go out to the pictures

with him. He also asked if Cherry was still as noisy
as ever, at which I promptly replied 'YES!!!'

Dear Mr Townsend, my favourite teacher at my primary school. I wrote a whole chapter about him in *Jacky Daydream* – and I was so touched when Mr Townsend wrote to me after it was published. He'd seen me on a television programme going round Latchmere, reminiscing happily about him. I was so pleased to be able to tell him just how much he meant to all of us.

I seemed to have an embarrassingly vast capacity for crushes. I went to the Adam Faith show with Carol on 21 February, the first time I'd ever been to a pop concert. It was a small gig by modern standards, on the stage of the Granada cinema, but I was bowled over:

The John Barry Seven were ever so good. You had to clap, you couldn't help it while the music pounded out, everyone was joining in the beat. I've never experienced anything like it, you don't feel at all self conscious, just madly <u>hep</u>. Of course Adam was wonderful. Honestly, I've never believed girls could scream so loud! Adam looked ever so handsome though!

I've stuck a photo of him on another page in my diary, with 'Adam for Always!' and 'Faith Forever' written in lurid green biro.

I still remembered Alan fondly, my first 'boyfriend' back at primary school.

Friday 26 February
Carol told me that she saw ALAN yesterday. Oh, how <u>clear</u> everything is now. Until she mentioned him, I didn't realise how much I <u>still</u> like him. Ken was just a substitute for ALAN because he reminded me a little of him (they both have fair hair, etc.). Likewise my fair Craig. Carol said ALAN had on a seaman's cap and a navy overcoat. He told me when he was ten that he was going in the Merchant Navy, but fancy him sticking to it. I expect he was home on leave.

Alan would only have been fourteen, the same age as me, but I think there was a special boy sailor entry into the Merchant Navy in those days.

Wednesday 2 March
Going home Carol and I reminisced about the old days at Latchmere.

185

Oh Alan.

Oh Alan, do you remember the dressing room up in the gallery where we used to go? Do you remember the purple velvet crinoline we found there that I dressed up in?

Do you remember our 'sunbathing' with Robert and Eileen, etc.?

Do you remember when I suddenly saw you looking at me, and we looked for a long time and then kissed?

Oh, I wish I was back at Latchmere.

I wasn't really in love with Alan, we'd just been children. I wasn't in love with Craig or Ken or Adam Faith. I was simply in love with the idea of being in love. I was fourteen and it was spring.

Sunday 6 March
I went to Y.F. this afternoon, wearing Mum's cream Spring coat. On the bus I noticed lots of signs that Spring is here. There were many pink apple blossom trees in full bloom. Malden bridge was being mended and the bus couldn't get through, so I had to walk part of the way, but I didn't mind. While we were singing the hymn at Y.F. John Reynolds kept on staring at me. Chris has had her

hair done; it looked very nice. Mr G talked about T.V. It was <u>very</u> interesting, especially when he talked about a programme about teenagers.

John Reynolds now?
I did still have a mind, in spite of all the boy-madness.

Monday 7 March
We had double Art with Mrs Canter. She suggested I take O level Art in my G.C.E. At the same time she pointed out that although my 'Picture of the corner of our living room' was technically good, it was uninteresting. I couldn't agree more about it being dull, but how can one make a window, a radiator, a chair, part of a wall and part of a ceiling look thrilling? Admittedly Van Gogh did a lovely enthralling oil painting of a chair, but I am <u>not</u> Vincent Van Gogh, a genius at Art. For Latin homework we had one sentence 'The Romans seized the Sabine women'. How funny, because last Tuesday I saw the picture in the National Gallery 'The Rape of the Sabines'. Now I know where the word 'rape' is derived from, as the polite word 'seized' in Latin is rapio. In Drama Club I had to be <u>three</u> people all at once!

That shouldn't have been too much of a problem. I was used to playing three versions of myself: I was the dippy boy-mad teenager; the giggly schoolgirl; and the real me, reading and writing in my own secret world.

In Youth Fellowship on Sunday 13 March:

Johnny told us about the hike next Sat. It sounds wonderful fun; Chris says I can have lunch at her house and then – off we go. I hope it will be as fun as the Tramps Party. Ken and Robin were discussing an 'all night' hike. I heard them say 'Two tents?' and give dirty little chuckles.

Saturday 19 March
!!!!! THE HIKE !!!!!
Oh the hike was SMASHING. I went over to Chris in the morning, bought a navy duffel bag and did homework. After dinner Chris and I packed our duffel bags and met Viv. We were a bit nervous, but Viv was as matter of fact as usual. Everyone arrived at Worcester Park Station, and then – we set off! We got out at Box Hill and walked the opposite way towards Ranmore Common. We got lost, and ended up at Abinger in the evening! It was very warm and not muddy, except for one place where it was just a sea of mud. I took a huge step, and all at once my

shoe fell off, and I was standing in the mud in my socks. John Reynolds got it for me, and got his trousers all muddy! I bet his mother cursed me! We went up this hill as steep as a mountain, covered with all brambles like a jungle, and as I scrabbled and grovelled in the earth I felt a hearty push from behind and John's voice, 'Up we go, Jacqueline!' We climbed over barbed wire, ate, and walked and walked until long past dark. Afterwards John Wilkins invited all 23 of us back to his house for coffee and biscuits. When we got there there weren't any empty chairs left, and Ken and Robin invited us to sit on their laps! I don't know which I like best now: Ken, John R or John W.

I think John R sounds a sweetie, wading into the mud to rescue my shoe! We might have stayed out after dark, but we certainly didn't stay out all night. We were all extremely well-behaved. I was rather prim and priggish at fourteen:

Monday 4 April
At dinner Janice B told us that Mr Gander [one of the French teachers] had suddenly said to them, 'Let's have a debate.' The girls in her group were approving as they were naturally willing to have a

break from French. One bright spark suggested they should have a debate on 'Should boys be allowed to do what they like with girls?' Mr Gander was <u>extremely willing</u>. He told them that he thought virginity is an important factor in marriage, and that although he and his wife had intercourse a few times before they were married, he didn't think we ought to. He went on in this way, and then asked if there were any questions. One girl asked 'Why does a woman not have a baby every time she does it?' He told them that if you do it a certain time after a girl's period nothing would probably happen. <u>Honestly, isn't he awful</u>. Janice said that towards the end he got awfully het up and excited. Ugh! I'm glad I don't have him for French. Give me Mrs Coffin every day, you bet. Angela and Irene said that they'd already done it with a boy once or twice, and seemed extremely proud of the fact. They'd have laughed the other sides of their faces if anything had happened.

I saw Craig again on 19 April:

In Kingston I saw Craig who was going into Maxwells. He somehow reminded me very much of a sailor in his blue jeans and shirt, and his fair hair.

Thursday 21 April
I caught the bus home and I saw Craig. Before this
week when I saw him I just thought of him like –
well, an ordinary boy, but today! Wham! Now
PLEASE don't think how awful I am, because I
keep on saying I'm crazy about different boys. I'll
explain. I like Jeremy H and John R and John W
but that is all, I don't particularly like them. At the
time I did like Ken a lot, but now I realise it was
only to keep Chris company. I always knew I could
never like him as much as she likes Peter. Now I
can understand her because I keep on thinking of
Craig and wanting to talk about him every minute
of the day. But don't be mistaken, Alan is still first
with me, and always will be, but it's no use thinking
about him as I'll probably never see him again,
whereas I see Craig every day.

Sue next door used to go to the same school as
Craig: 'She told me he likes Art and History best.
I know he must like swimming for I often see him
go out with a towel tucked under his arm.'
I was like a Mickey Mouse detective, observing,
questioning, following a boy who was serenely
unaware of my existence. I was still interested in
a handful of Youth Fellowship boys. We went for
another hike:

Saturday 30 April

I met Chris at 10 a.m., and we wandered around the shops and went to the park. After dinner we met Carol and went to Worcester Park station. Mr and Mrs Golden and their son and their dog Rory came on the hike. We went to Box Hill station again, and climbed up Box Hill. Then we walked, ditto, ditto, ditto. Luckily it was not muddy this time, in fact it was very dry. This time we had to make our way down a chalk cliff on a neighbouring hill. Rory kept on breaking loose, and J.W. in relation to Rory's lead said 'Grab his whatsit,' and K.W. said 'I beg your pardon!' Everyone swapped jokes, and on the train back there was a paper fight between one compartment and the next. Afterwards we went back to J.W.'s house and watched T.V. and had coffee. Chris and I talked a bit to B.T., J.R. and Pyjamas. J.R. called us both by our names.

Sunday 1 May

I stayed in bed this morning, and after a good read, quickly skimmed through my Latin book. It's amazing the amount I've forgotten. Still, not to worry. In the afternoon I went to Y.F. and Mr Golden talked about 'Tough Guys'. As I sat there while Mr G talked on and on I imagined Mr G in Heaven, with a little golden halo perched on his head. It got very hot in that stuffy little room, and the atmosphere seemed to press down on me. The hard little chairs are very uncomfortable and I couldn't help fidgeting; first with my handbag, crossing my legs, rocking my chair, looking at Chris and J.R., at the ceiling, at the wall. The blue of the cloth on the table, the pink of the wall, the white of the ceiling, and the grey of the boys' clothes all swam together, and I felt dizzy. Then my eyes began to water and I had to rub them. My throat was dry and parched, and I couldn't swallow, my lips felt as if they would never open again and I had to keep wetting them. Oh the blessed relief when we began the hymn!

Sunday 8 May
In the morning Mum and I stayed in bed for a while and Daddy went to tennis. It was very, very hot and in the afternoon I only wore my green shirtwaister. It was the Sunday School's anniversary and instead of the usual Y.F. service we all went down into the church and listened to the children's service in which the Juniors took part. Geraldine Webb, Ken's sister, sang a solo. (She has a nice clear little voice.) I was sitting sandwiched between Carol and John Reynolds. Carol wore her new black and white checked dress again. After the service I said goodbye to Carol and Viv and went to tea at Chris's.

We decided to go for a walk and took little-girl-next-door Margaret's dog Bluey. She is a lovely, very energetic, cocker spaniel. We took her to Beverly Brook which was crowded with New Maldenites. We went past all these boys who made noises after us, and immediately almost bumped into Ken Webb and Robin Marriot! After tea we re-met Carol and Viv and returned to church. Mr Golden is getting quite pally with us and called me 'Jac' and was very concerned about Carol's cold. We all wore lily of the valley posies on our dresses as they are our church's special flower. In the evening service it was the Seniors' turn to perform and they acted the part of nurses, beggars, school children, etc. Dangling from the roof of the church was a painted sun, moon and some clouds and stars to represent the universe, and every time Mr Kelly or anyone got up to preach they got hit on the head by the sun.

I still didn't seem to be making proper friends with any of these boys.

Monday 20 June
I must admit it would be nice to have a boyfriend to boast about, but boys of my own age are so stupid, and boys of about 16 or 17 who are interested in

194

girls want girls their own age. Oh well, if I'm just patient I expect one will come along some day.

I had lots of attention from the wrong sort of boy. Whenever Carol and I went to the pictures, older boys usually started whistling or messing around or trying out some corny chat-up line. Carol looked older than me and had a dark, pouty, smouldering look they found very attractive. But we both found these approaches embarrassing and we were under no illusions – they just wanted girls to sit in the back row with them. We knew what was likely to happen.

Tuesday 9 August
In the afternoon Carol and I went to the Granada to see 'Make Mine Mink'. It was very very funny, but half the time we weren't watching the screen, but watching the couple in front of us. A girl was sitting in the middle of the row and a boy at the end. The girl got up to go, and as she passed him the boy looked at her. A few minutes later the girl returned, only this time she sat next to him. They started talking, and he gave her a cigarette. Then he casually put his arm along the back of her seat, and then onto her shoulder. Then he leant over and kissed her, then again. She leant back and he leant

over her and they kissed and kissed passionately. Then he slowly slid his hand up her skirt but I don't think she liked that because she tried to push it away. Anyway, when the film ended the boy whispered to the girl, and then went out and didn't come back. The girl sat placidly in front of us and watched the second film. Two perfect strangers!

Boys tried to pick girls up everywhere.

Friday 22 April
I met Carol at half past two and we went to the baths, but they were packed, and there was a very long queue. We resolutely joined the end of it. A Teddy boy ran his hand up my back and I said 'Do you mind?' and dragged Carol away as I <u>hate</u> that sort of boy.

Teddy boys wore their hair in greasy quiffs, they had long fancy jackets down to their knees, bootlace ties, drainpipe trousers and suede shoes with enormous soles. They were nearly all harmless suburban lads, but the very name 'teddy boy' made Biddy think of flick-knives and drinking and sex and doing a ton on motorbikes. She wanted me to find a boyfriend but she'd have fainted if I'd brought home a teddy boy.

Sunday 17 July
Went to Burnham Beeches with Carol. At the swimming pool a boy squirted water from a soda siphon all over us. Then we went round the fair together. I turned round, and noticed that four teds were following. Cas and I walked on to the Rollapenny and the teds followed and stood very close behind us. One of them said, 'I dunno how to play Rollapenny, perhaps one of these young ladies will show us how' so I said, 'Okay, if you provide the pennies.' And believe it or not the ted fished in his pocket and brought out a handful of coppers. I felt awful (I don't know why) so I didn't take any.

This was all pretty tame, but sometimes girls felt very vulnerable back in 1960, when mild sexual harassment was commonplace:

Thursday 4 August
Went to Lagoon with Carol. Four boys kept throwing matches at us and kept on talking for hours. I didn't like them and neither did Carol but we stayed until

one of them mentioned undoing my swimming costume zip, and then we hastily departed.

Monday 8 August
Carol and I went to the Lagoon, but the changing rooms were being sluiced out all day so we had to change in the open. It was horrible. When I had nothing on but a towel on my top some men came along and stared and commented.

I was starting to despair. There were a good handful of boys I liked, but none of them seemed to want to get to know me properly. All the boys who showed an interest in me were too old or too scary or too crude. But at the end of August Biddy and Harry and I went on holiday to Cornwall – and I had my first real romance.

GOOD LUCK

FROM ST IVES

12
Cornwall

We went on a fortnight's holiday, one week in St Ives and one week in Newquay, with Uncle Ron and Aunty Grace. I wonder whose idea it was. Biddy worked with Ron at Prince Machines and they were very close. I'm sure they'd have loved to go off on holiday, just the two of them. It seemed so strange for us all to go in this awkward fivesome. Why didn't Harry or Grace object? I didn't mind for myself. I'd been to Cornwall before on an odd holiday with Harry and had thought it beautiful. (He and Biddy had separate holidays the year I was eleven – I had to accompany both of them in turn.)

Cornwall was considered *exotic* in 1960, before there were cheap package tours abroad. Chris was going on holiday to Eastbourne as usual with Fred, Hetty and Jan. I think Carol and her family were just having day trips here and there.

I met up with Carol the Friday before we went on holiday and we went to the Boys and Girls Exhibition at Olympia. I'd been there before when I was younger, with Biddy. I'd shyly whispered a few words to the children's author Pamela Brown and been traumatized by George Cansdale wrapping a large snake round my neck. I kept well away from any animal stand this time.

I looked hopefully for Pamela Brown, or indeed any other authors. I have a feeling Noel Streatfeild might have been there. I'd loved all Noel Streatfeild's books when I was younger and longed to see her, even if I wasn't sure I'd have enough gump to talk to her – not without Biddy prodding me into action. But we couldn't find Noel Streatfeild. It was hard finding any of the stands it was so jam-packed. We simply shuffled here, stumbled there, eating hot dogs for our lunch, giggling and blushing when any boys spoke to us.

When I got home Biddy had done all my packing for me. She spent hours ironing and folding and arranging every item in perfect patterns until each suitcase looked like a work of art. My white canvas beach shoes and my new pointy black heels touched toes beside my blue and white floral swimming costume and my best baby-doll pyjamas; my underwear was prinked into shape like elaborate table napkins; my two white T-shirts and my startlingly short shorts were carefully folded, still serenely spotless. My pale lilac cardigan was curled round them like a little furry creature, and all my frocks were puffed out and folded over tissue paper: my green shirtwaister and a deep blue floral frock and a new white puff-sleeved dress sprigged with tiny apricot flowers. My favourite lilac skirt floated on top, freshly laundered and immaculately ironed.

'Oh thanks, Mum, but what about my *stuff*? My journal and my notebook and my black folder and—'

'You're not going to be huddled in a corner writing all day long. You're on *holiday*,' said Biddy.

'But what about my books?'

'You can take a paperback for the train,' said Biddy. 'We'll get you some magazines too.'

I didn't argue, knowing it was a waste of breath. I waited until she'd gone to tackle Harry's packing – he wasn't trusted to do it himself either – and then carefully shoved my diary down in the depths of the case, together with *The Greengage Summer*, a Monica Dickens paperback, a little Collins copy of *Jane Eyre* because it was very long. *Gone with the Wind* because it was even longer, and my current favourite book for the train, *Billy Liar* by Keith Waterhouse.

I found *Billy Liar* riveting reading. It's a story about a young Yorkshire lad called Billy Fisher who worked in an undertaker's, had three simultaneous girlfriends and told compulsive lies. I was a suburban schoolgirl who didn't even have one boyfriend and didn't tell *actual* lies, though I was frequently economical with the truth. I identified totally with Billy because he was a helpless daydreamer, forever seeking refuge in his own imaginary world of Ambrosia, he didn't feel he fitted in with his family, and he badly wanted to be a writer. It was a revelation to me that someone else felt exactly the same way I did. I laughed at his jokes, I bit my lip when he got into endless trouble, I learned all his catch phrases, I lived every minute of his life.

Biddy sniffed when she saw me clutching *Billy Liar* the next morning and Harry cursed when he picked up my suitcase (*Gone with the Wind* alone was like a couple of bricks), but I couldn't bear the thought of running out of reading matter. I had two long weeks sitting on a beach with four adults who would be talking amongst themselves. It's a wonder I didn't try to stuff our collected hardback edition of Jane Austen into my suitcase too.

I read my way through *Billy Liar* twice on the train journey down to St Ives. It was always an incredible palaver for the three of us travelling anywhere. Ron and Grace must have travelled separately by car. We certainly had the use of a car on holiday and it wasn't ours. It would probably have been too much of a squash for all of us to travel down to Cornwall in Ron's car, especially as we three Aitkens travelled with four large cumbersome cases and several bags and carriers as well. Biddy had to have *two* large battered Revelation suitcases to spread her frocks out properly, fluttering brightly in between layers of tissue paper like giant butterflies.

We would normally have taken the hourly Green Line bus all the way up to London but we couldn't possibly manhandle so much luggage ourselves so we hired a car up to Paddington. This was such an extraordinary step that Biddy and Harry were extra tense on the journey, and I sat bolt upright, eyes closed, breathing shallowly, praying that I wasn't going to be sick over the hired upholstery.

We felt triumphant when we eventually flopped down on the scratchily upholstered seats in the train. Poor Harry struggled to stow all the cases in the roof racks while Biddy fussed because we weren't facing the engine and pulled hard on the leather strap to make sure the window was tightly closed. It was stifling in the carriage before we'd even started the journey, but she was anxious about smuts flying in and speckling our virgin-white shirts and cardigans with soot. This was the age of steam trains. They let fly a plume of white smoke as they chugged through the countryside, the wheels turning to a comforting tune: *diddle-de-der*, *diddle-de-der*, *diddle-de-der*, on and on. And on and on and *on*, all the way to St Ives.

It took all day long then. By the time we eventually arrived and checked into our modest hotel we were exhausted. We met up with Ron and Grace and ate our dinner of brown Windsor soup, boiled beef and carrots, and vanilla ice cream with tinned peaches, and then went straight to our bedroom.

We had to unpack everything there and then and hang it up carefully under Biddy's strict supervision. I quickly hid my extra books in the drawer she'd designated for my T-shirts and underwear. I had my journal and was all set to write up the day while Biddy and Harry were making their treks to the bathroom and back. The hotel was quite posh in our eyes but certainly didn't run to en suite bathrooms. I was so tired I just wrote in pencil: 'Long long long train journey', and then I fell asleep.

We met up with Ron and Grace again at breakfast, Biddy and Ron chatting animatedly, Harry and Grace chewing silently, me spooning up my tinned grapefruit and surreptitiously peering round at all the other guests in the dining room. There didn't seem to be any girls my age. There *were* a few boys, but surprisingly none particularly took my eye.

I was keen to get to the beach. We sunbathed most of Sunday. I wore my minuscule short shorts and white top and later changed into my blue and white swimsuit. Biddy wore her very similar costume on the beach. There are snapshot photos of us looking alarmingly alike, our brown hair blown back by the breeze, showing our high foreheads, our big noses and determined chins. Biddy is small and slim and looks years younger than her age. It must have been galling for Grace, who was older and stockier and much more staid looking. There are no photos of her in her swimming costume.

There are lots of photos of Ron, who is older and overweight and very homely looking, with eyes too close together and flat Brylcreemed hair – and yet he's always got a cheery grin on his face and the only time he's bothered to try to suck in his stomach is when he's standing in the sea with Harry and me.

Harry is the best looking of all of us, his tennis playing keeping him trim and muscular. He tanned easily, going an impressive golden brown within a couple of days. He's smiling in every photo too, which seems astonishing.

On the Monday we had a trip out in Ron's car to Mullion and the Lizard. I was particularly enthusiastic about going to Mullion because I'd once enjoyed reading a book by Mabel Esther Allan about a bunch of children with bizarre names: there was one girl with green eyes called Pussy, and the narrator was called Mullion after the Cornish cove. The Lizard sounded interesting too. I was mad enough to hope for real large lizards lurking on the rocks like a fantasy Jurassic age. Both Mullion and the Lizard were doubtless beautiful but a little disappointing in reality. I'm not sure which is which in the little black and white snapshots. There's one of a vast cliff with Ron straddling a large rock, flabby chest and big belly making him look like a Buddha.

We made another trip out to Land's End. In those days it was attractively bare and deserted so it gave you a feeling of being at the very end of England. The only nod to tourism was a signpost where you could insert the letters of your own home town. So there we are, smiling under a sign that said CHEAM 291 MILES (where Ron and Grace lived) and KINGSTON 283 MILES.

We all look relaxed and are smiling obediently, even Harry and Grace. Harry is wearing a too-tight sweater, baggy tennis shorts and open-toed sandals, *not* a good look. Grace is sitting down, wearing a large frock, skirts blowing in the breeze, a bead necklace round her throat. Biddy is next to her, her grinning mouth dark with lipstick. She's wearing a snug sweater and surprising trousers – she called them trews – in a jazzy zigzag pattern. Ron is standing above her, one arm leaning on the signpost, the other arm round me. My shorts look indecent, I'm showing way too much plump leg. I was always such an anxious, self-conscious girl, fussing desperately over my hair, obsessing about a tiny spot on my nose – how could I have gone out practically showing my knickers?

Our hotel held a dance on Monday evening. I wasn't sure I wanted to go, feeling foolish trailing behind these four ill-assorted adults.

'Can't I just stay in my room and read?' I begged Biddy.

'No, of course you can't! You can't just lurk in the bedroom and read. You're here to enjoy yourself on holiday,' said Biddy.

I *wasn't* enjoying myself. I felt bored and restless and embarrassed trailing round with four adults all the time, and I was terribly aware of Grace's little huffs and Harry's sulks. We were playing this game that we were all great friends having a fantastic holiday, but we all knew that wasn't true.

'I don't want to go to this damn daft dance either,' said Harry. 'I'm going to push off for a walk.'

'You can't! You've *got* to come,' Biddy said, craning to zip herself into her best low-necked frock.

'I haven't *got* to do anything. I don't want to dance with you – and I certainly don't want to dance with Grace,' said Harry.

'You've got to, to be polite. Look, don't just stand there, help me with my zip!'

Harry sorted her out so smartly that the skin of her back got pinched in the zip. Biddy screamed and accused him of doing it on purpose. There was a row, conducted in whispers, because all the bedrooms were in close proximity. Harry stormed off on his walk. Biddy collapsed in tears. I tried inadequately to comfort her, longing to escape back into my book.

But disaster was averted. Harry came back twenty minutes later. He wasn't talking, but he put on a clean white shirt and changed into his best grey suit. Biddy held a damp flannel over her eyes and then patted her powder in place, painting a big lipstick smile on her face. I stopped lolling on my bed with my book and shook out my creased skirts. My white dress set off my tan and I had a new gilt and mother-of-pearl locket as a holiday present.

We lined up to peer in the big mirror inside the wardrobe, Biddy and Harry and me, and we all passed muster. Then we went down the stairs, along the passageway and into the ballroom to join up with Ron and Grace, who were already halfway through their lemonade shandies.

Oh, those long-ago dances! You had a waltz, a quickstep, a slow foxtrot, and if you were really dashing, a cha-cha-cha. There were the novelty dances, the spot waltz where the music stopped every few minutes and the compère asked a silly question and the first couple to answer it got a prize: a bar of chocolate or a tin of talcum powder or a propelling pencil, nothing exciting at all, but the couples whooped as if they'd won the football pools. Then there was the Paul Jones, where all the ladies joined hands in a circle facing outwards and all the gentlemen formed an outer circle facing inwards, holding hands far more awkwardly. When the music started the ladies danced clockwise, the men anti-clockwise, until the music stopped and you had to dance with the man facing you. Sometimes there were more ladies than men and you got a gap, so you had to slink back to your seat until the circles started up again.

But I was lucky that evening. I wrote: 'I had a partner for nearly all the dances, but I'm not particularly keen on any of the boys here although they are really very nice.'

'Very nice' sounds a little limp. I was obviously still feeling depressed. Harry was very quiet too, though he did dance with Biddy several times, and even steered Grace around the room in a jerky quickstep. Biddy and Ron danced too. I wonder if those snatched five-minute sessions on the dance floor made the whole holiday worthwhile.

But the next evening:

we went for a walk around Zennor head. First we climbed up a very high stony hill which was covered with very soft earthy grass that looked rather like lava from a volcano. When you reached the top a tremendously powerful wind almost lifted you off the peak, so that I experienced a sensation almost equal to flying. The wind seemed to cleanse and lift my spirits until I was almost bubbling over.

I can still vividly remember staring up at the stars and wanting to spread my arms and leap upwards.

'Then we went for a walk along the cliff in the dark and poor Uncle Ron tripped over and sprained his ankle.'

Did he trip – or was he pushed? Did Harry bump into him accidentally on purpose? Did Grace shove him with a sharp elbow? What were we *doing*, walking along a clifftop in the dark?

But we all got back to St Ives safe and sound, though Ron limped for a few days and wasn't able to trip the light fantastic at the farewell dance on Friday night.

We moved on to Newquay on the Saturday, all booked up for one more week. I'd much sooner have gone straight home to Cumberland House, where I could have a bit of privacy in my own bedroom, read and write whenever I felt like it, and go to the pictures or the shops or the lagoon with Chris or Carol. I even fantasized about seizing my train ticket from Biddy's purse and travelling home on the train by myself.

I tried suggesting this in a very roundabout way – 'It's been a lovely holiday but I'm a bit worried, I didn't take any of my school set work. Tell you what, I could always go home a bit early and get on with it. You don't have to worry about me, you know I *like* being by myself, and I could have my dinners at Ga's, she wouldn't mind a bit.'

'Don't be so *silly!*' said Biddy. 'Come on, start getting your things laid out nicely on your bed for me to pack. You're coming with us.'

'But I don't want to,' I mumbled childishly.

'Well, that's just too bad,' said Biddy. 'Now get cracking with those clothes, pronto, and stop being so ruddy ungrateful. *I* never went away on holiday for a whole two weeks when I was your age. Stop pulling that sulky face. You'll love it when you get there.'

She was right, oh so right!

On Newquay beach

Harry, Jacqueline and Ron

Cookie, his sister and Colin

13

Cookie

Saturday 27 August
Our new landlady, Mrs Philpotts, is an absolute
scream of a character, although she means very well.
She is a very hearty type with an enormous bust
and a horsy face. I think I'm going to like Newquay
and this hotel better than St Ives. The young people
are – two teenage blondes that are nicknamed 'The
Beverley Sisters', a big hefty boy called Jeff, and a
nice-looking boy about 13–14 called Colin, with his
sister and his sister's friend, both called Gillian
and both 16.

I never got to know the Beverley Sisters or big
hefty Jeff – but I *did* get to know Colin.

I got up early on Sunday morning and wandered
downstairs a good half-hour before the breakfast
gong. Mrs Philpotts had said there was a recreation
room with a small library. I still had *Gone with the
Wind* as a standby but I wanted to see what other
books were on offer. I peeped in several doors and
found the dining room all set up for breakfast and

a sitting room with big sofas and a small television set – and then I stumbled upon the recreation room. It was just a small room with a shelf of Agatha Christie and Alistair Maclean paperbacks and a lot of board games, Monopoly and Ludo and Snakes and Ladders. There was a table-tennis table crammed into the room – and Colin was standing at the net, madly trying to play his left hand against his right hand.

He grinned when he saw me and clapped his tennis bats together. 'Hurray! Come and play with me!' he said, as if we'd known each other for ever.

'I can't play. I don't know how,' I said.

'I'll teach you,' said Colin, thrusting the bat in my hand.

'I'm not any good at games,' I said. 'I'm sure I'll be hopeless.'

I *was* hopeless, but Colin didn't seem to mind. He was happy to chase after the ball and win spectacularly.

'*Champion, the wonder horse!*' he sang. (It was the theme tune from a children's television show.) He threw back his head and neighed while I giggled uncertainly.

'You are daft,' I said.

'Course I am. Totally nuts,' said Colin happily. 'I'm Colin. What's your name?'

'Jacky.'

'Have you got any brothers or sisters here?'

I shook my head.

'I've got my big sister Gillian. She's with *her* friend Gillian. She's OK but she's sixteen, too old for me. How old are you, Jacky?'

'Fourteen.'

'Well, I'm *nearly* fourteen. Do you want to be my girlfriend?'

I stared at him. I liked him but I didn't want a boyfriend who was younger than me – and totally nuts.

'Let's just be friends,' I said cautiously.

'OK,' said Colin, not seeming to mind. 'I've got this friend Cookie. He's a great laugh. He's got this beach hut. We muck around together. Maybe you could be *his* girlfriend?'

'I don't think so!'

Cookie! He sounded as odd as Colin. I didn't think it at all likely I'd want to be his girlfriend.

'Well, you could still come and hang out with us by the beach hut,' Colin suggested.

'It's very kind of you, but I'm here with my parents and their friends,' I mumbled. 'Shall we have another game of table tennis?'

'Yeah, yeah, great,' said Colin, immediately serving and not even giving me a chance to return the ball. 'One to me. Are you going to the beach today then?'

'Yes, I expect so.'

'Are you going to do any surfriding?'

'You bet,' I said.

He looked surprised and wiggled his eyebrows. 'You can really surf?'

'Of course I can,' I said proudly.

I'd been to Newquay two years before and surfed every day. *Not* the surfriding guys in wetsuits do today, standing up and zigzagging over huge breakers. I wish! No, in 1960 in England, surfriding meant basic wooden boards. As long as you were a strong swimmer anyone could wade out, wait for a big wave, lie on the board and be whisked along into the shallows. I might be a total duffer at table tennis but I loved swimming and I'd taken to surfriding in a big way.

'Two to me. My pal Cookie's super at surfing. I'm just sort of so-so,' said Colin. 'I don't like getting my head under the water.' He shook his thick brown hair, pulling a silly face. Then his eyes brightened.

'So what kind of swimming costume have you got, Jacky?' he said, serving again. The ball whizzed straight past me. 'Come on, you can't be *that* bad . . . Is it a bikini?' he added hopefully.

'No, it's *not* a bikini,' I said.

'Oh, spoilsport,' said Colin. As he served he

started singing the 'Itsy Bitsy Teenie Weenie Yellow Polka Dot Bikini' song.

'Mine's a swimsuit. It's not itsy-bitsy or teeny-weeny, and it's not even yellow, it's blue and white,' I said. I actually managed to connect bat with ball and smash it past him.

The breakfast gong sounded and Colin grinned.

'Just as you were coming into your own. Oh well, maybe see you on the beach? Or if not, come and find us along the beach-hut terrace. Cookie's hut is number sixty-eight.' He put his head on one side, squinting at me earnestly. 'You're absolutely *sure* you don't want to be my girlfriend?'

I was still absolutely sure, but I did like Colin a lot. He waved to me enthusiastically when I entered the breakfast room with Biddy and Harry, calling, 'Hello Jacky!' nearly knocking his orange juice over.

'I see you've made a friend here already, Jac!' said Biddy.

'We just played table tennis together,' I said casually.

'You played table tennis?' said Harry, raising his eyebrows. He'd tried very hard one summer to teach me the rudiments of tennis, with spectacular lack of success.

'I'm not very good at it,' I said humbly.

'Never mind, as if it matters,' said Biddy. 'It's

lovely that you're chumming up with someone. You never know, you *might* meet up with him on the beach.' She sounded a little patronizing.

'Well, his friend's got a beach hut. He wanted me to go there, practically begged me,' I said. 'But I'm not sure I want to. In fact I definitely don't.'

'Oh, *Jac*,' said Biddy, exasperated. 'I don't understand you at all.'

I didn't really understand myself. I'd been so fed up traipsing around with Biddy and Harry and Ron and Grace. Now I had a chance of younger, livelier, albeit crazier company and I was wilfully turning it down. I suppose I was just a bit shy, a bit scared. You couldn't be shy or scared of Colin but this unknown Cookie might be a different matter.

So I ignored Colin's gesturing queries and went off to get ready for a day on the beach with Biddy and Harry and Ron and Grace. This involved a lot of packing. Biddy had her favourite Evan Hunter book and her spare white cardigan and her camera and her swimming costume, just in case. Harry had his racing papers and his windcheater and his woolly swimming trunks and a spare towel snaffled from the hotel bedroom. Ron and Grace took beach time even more seriously. Ron had his trunks and his own big stripy towel and his hairbrush and Brylcreem and a beach ball and a big bag of toffees.

Grace had her knitting and a map of Cornwall and a thermos and plastic cups and a damp cloth in a plastic bag and a *Woman's Own*. I had my swimming costume and *Jane Eyre* and my journal.

We wandered down to the beach, lugging our burdens. I saw the rows of beach huts and hesitated for a moment, but I scurried off after the others. I hoped they might settle on the smooth golden sand near the beach huts but they seemed intent on doing a Lawrence of Arabia trek across the sands, seeking an ideal spot.

We eventually set up camp way down the beach, out of sight of the beach huts. I pretended I didn't care. I struggled into my swimming costume under cover of my towel and then lay on my tummy, reading and eating Ron's toffees. Ron tried to tempt us with a game of ball, and for a little while he and Harry tossed it about while I was piggy in the middle. Biddy and Grace made strained conversation while peering at the map, plotting little outings to Polperro and Mousehole and Jamaica Inn.

There were families all around us, some of the boys rushing in surfing.

'Shall we give this surfing lark a go?' Ron asked eagerly. 'Come on, Biddy, I bet you're a dab hand at it. Get your costume on!'

'No, no, I'm much too comfortable,' said Biddy.

'Jac, you'll have a go, won't you? I'll show you what to do,' said Ron.

'Jac's a good surfer already,' Harry said coldly. 'I showed her how on our last holiday to Newquay.'

This was a downright lie. Harry was a weak swimmer and didn't have much clue how to surf, but I smiled at him loyally. The three of us trailed all the way to the surf shack to hire boards. No one bothered to ask poor Grace if she'd like a go.

I clutched my board and waded gingerly into the water, lifting my feet high and jumping every time a wave swelled past me, a total wimp about getting wet. But though it took me ages to get in properly up to my neck, with Harry and Ron shouting and splashing me, I came into my own once I was in. I paddled around on my surfboard, eyeing up each likely wave, and then, just before it crested, I leaped forward and hurtled full tilt all the way into the shallows. I waded out again and again, while Harry and Ron wobbled and wavered and fell off their boards.

Biddy came picking her way to the water's edge, her Brownie camera in her hand. She lined us up and commanded us to smile, bossily intent – so much so that she shrieked when a wave suddenly swirled round her ankles, wetting the hem of her frock. We all smiled easily enough then.

I hated the getting-out-the-water stage, blue and shivering, with the towel wrapped around me, struggling out of my wet costume and into my knickers, trying not to get everything all sandy. But the sun was out and I gratefully drank a cup of tea from Grace's thermos. I combed my straggly hair and fished my coral lipstick out of the pocket of my skirt.

'Haven't we got any sandwiches?' said Ron, rubbing his big tummy. 'I'm starving after all that surfing. Let's have a picnic.'

'Oh, Ron, how can I make up a picnic when we're staying in a hotel?' said Grace.

'*I'll* magic up a picnic,' said Ron, reaching for his wallet. 'I'll nip along the beach to the shops. Who's coming with me to help carry the goodies?'

He looked hopefully at Biddy, but she was stretched out, eyes closed, seemingly asleep. Ron looked at me instead. 'Come on, Jacky.'

So I sauntered along beside him, carrying my sandals, while he laughed and joked and clowned around. He attempted daft conjuring tricks, plucking pennies from my ears, hankies from my hair. People on the beach smiled at us, obviously thinking he was my dad. In lots of ways I wished he *was* my dad. You could laugh and joke and tease him back, you never had to be wary, you could say the first thing that came into your head.

I wrote later, cruelly:

How happy we'd all be if Uncle Ron and Mum married. Dad would have Aunty Grace! (Two awkward ones together.) I am writing a lot of nasty things about him, we haven't had a quarrel or anything but I'm just fed up and truthfully admitting things I've loyally tried to ignore. Later I'll probably want to tear out this page. But if Daddy wasn't my father I wouldn't be the same, as I am very like him in some ways.

I know Biddy tried to read my diary, which was why I kept trying to find new hiding places for it. I do so hope Harry didn't ever find it and read that last passage. Today I went through many files of my old manuscripts, looking for the story I wrote about that Cornish holiday. I came across two letters that Harry wrote to me when I was living in Scotland several years later – lovely, funny, stylish letters that made me want to cry. I couldn't find the story anywhere, though I did find a letter telling me that it had won a competition, the first time I'd ever won anything with my writing. But I don't really need to find that story. I can still remember the holiday as if it was only last summer.

Ron and I went to the general shop and bought five big Cornish pasties, five Scotch eggs, five packets of Bovril-flavoured crisps, two pounds of tomatoes, a bunch of bananas and a bag of apples. He dawdled at the sweet counter and then chose five Fry's Five Boys chocolate bars. There were faces of the five boys on the wrapper, labelled DESPERATION, PACIFICATION, EXPECTATION, ACCLAMATION, REALIZATION. Uncle Ron imitated each one with his big red rubbery features, making everyone in the shop chuckle.

There was a particularly loud hoot of a laugh behind me, curiously familiar. I turned round. There was Colin, choking on his choc ice, standing beside a boy with intense brown eyes, fair curly hair and a smooth golden tan. He was wearing a casual white shirt and blue shorts and his sandy feet were bare. I stared at him and he stared at me.

'This is *Jacky* – you know, the girl I told you about. We played ping-pong this morning,' said Colin. 'I won, both games. Jacky, this is my friend Cookie.'

I swallowed. I smiled. Cookie put his hand out in a charmingly old-fashioned way, shaking mine.

'Hello. Colin's told me all about you. I'm Peter Cookson, but all my friends call me Cookie.'

Did that mean I could call him Cookie too? What exactly had Colin told him? Had he told him I didn't want to be his girlfriend?

Uncle Ron was wiggling his eyebrows and beaming at us, clutching our two big brown carrier bags.

'Are you Jacky's dad?' asked Colin.

'No, he's my . . . Uncle Ron,' I said.

'OK, Uncle Ron, can Jacky come and hang out with us over at the beach huts?' said Colin.

'Well, that's fine with me, but I expect she should ask her mum first. And she's got to come back up the beach with me for her picnic lunch.'

'She could have a picnic at our hut. My mum always has heaps,' said Cookie.

'Or we could come with you and wait till she's had her picnic and then walk back with her,' said Colin, licking the last of his choc ice from the wrapper.

So they ambled along beside us. My heart was beating fast underneath my white T-shirt. It was wonderful having not one but two boys begging for my company – and Cookie seemed so *special*.

Biddy sat up and blinked when we got back to our little camp. There I was, a boy on either side of me. Harry looked startled, Grace mildly surprised. Uncle Ron did the introductions and Colin sat down cross-legged at once and started chatting nineteen to the dozen. Cookie was much quieter, though he politely answered all Biddy's

226

questions. He lived in Sale, he was fifteen years old, he went to a grammar school.

'Mum!' I mumbled. She'd be asking him what his father did for a living next.

Grace took over the picnic, arranging pasties and Scotch eggs on the paper bags and circling them with tomatoes. I was so excited I just nibbled at a Scotch egg and then an apple.

'Don't you like pasties, Jacky? I *love* them,' said Colin blatantly.

Grace offered him one and he wolfed it down.

'I don't suppose there are any crisps going spare?' he said.

Cookie had a few crisps too, and then stood up. 'So it's OK if Jacky comes with us this afternoon?' he asked Biddy. 'We're number sixty-eight if you need to come and find her. Otherwise I'll walk her back to your hotel by six – is that all right?'

'*I'll* walk her, seeing as it's my hotel too,' said Colin.

'Well, just so long as *one* of you gets her back safely. She's such a daydreamer, she'd never find her way back on her own,' said Biddy, but she was smiling. 'Off you go then.'

I ran off with Cookie and Colin. We walked along the water's edge, suddenly all of us at a loss for words, even Colin. He started messing around, barging into Cookie, splashing him, trying to

227

wrestle with him. I edged away, not wanting to get my lilac skirt splashed. Maybe I should have changed back into my swimming costume? No, maybe not. They both stared at me a bit too much as it was.

'What's up, Jacky? Come in paddling,' said Colin, kicking his way through the waves.

'I don't want to get all wet again,' I said.

'Have you been swimming this morning then?' Cookie asked.

'Yep. Well, surfriding,' I said.

'She's really good at it,' said Colin, though he'd never seen me.

'So are you a really sporty girl then?'

'No fear! I *hate* most sports. It's my worst thing at school,' I said. 'I can't catch a ball and I can't run for toffee.'

'But you like swimming?'

'Yes, I love it.'

'Maybe you're a mermaid,' said Cookie. 'Perhaps you've got green scales under your pretty skirt.'

We both blushed. Colin sighed and went tearing along, kicking hard, lost in a plume of spray.

The sun came out from behind a cloud and shone on the blue water. I looked at the sea, the sky, the sands.

'It's so lovely here,' I said.

'I know. We come every year.' Cookie looked up

the beach to the rocks. 'There are caves in there. We could go exploring.'

'I don't think I've ever been in a proper cave before. Do they go back a long way?'

'Some of them do. When I was little I used to like setting up camp in them. I'd take a rug and my spade and some chocolate and stuff and crouch there in the dark, kidding on I was in some Enid Blyton book.'

'*The Cave of Adventure*! I read heaps of those. I love reading. Not Enid Blyton now, of course.'

'What do you like reading now then?' asked Cookie.

I had enough sense not to try and answer him properly as it would have taken all afternoon.

'I've just read a book called *Billy Liar*,' I said.

'Oh, I've read that,' said Cookie. 'It's good, isn't it. Funny. Those calendars!'

He really *had* read it.

'I wish he'd gone to London in the end,' I said.

'I'm going to go to London one day,' said Cookie. 'And I'll come and visit you and we'll go to . . . ?' He looked at me for suggestions.

'We'll go to all the coffee bars and jazz cellars in Soho,' I said, as if I frequented them every day. I thought hard, remembering my trips to the Royal Dental Hospital. 'And we'll have a meal at the

Golden Egg in Leicester Square and then go dancing at the Empire Ballroom.'

'Jiving,' said Cookie, suddenly taking hold of my hand and whirling me round.

'Come *on*, you two,' Colin yelled. 'What are you *doing*?'

'We're dancing,' said Cookie.

'Oh, right. OK, so am I,' said Colin, and he started capering around too, splashing more than ever.

It took us ages to get to the beach hut, but Cookie's parents seemed entirely unfazed. His dad just smiled and waved at Colin and me and then went back to his paper. His mum went into the beach hut and brought back four cans of Tizer and a mound of egg sandwiches in a big Oxo tin. The fourth can was for Cookie's sister, a shy, sweet girl several years younger than me. She looked admiringly at my flowery skirt and coral lipstick. My heart was beating fast again. I wasn't the shy young girl this time. I was the older girl with the cool clothes and make-up, the one the boys liked.

We ate and drank and then played a silly game of deck quoits, where luckily you didn't need much skill at all. Then Cookie and Colin and I went down the beach near the sea where the sand was firm and started making a giant boat with some old spades that had been propped up inside the beach hut. Colin dug wildly of course, flinging sand over his shoulder, but he had bags of energy and got a lot done. Cookie was good at organizing the shape of the boat, smoothing and sculpting carefully. I wandered around collecting shells to stud the sides of the boat and carved stylized waves all around it.

It took us *hours* but it was a truly magnificent boat by the time we'd finished it. We clambered gingerly inside on the sand seat, begging Colin to be extra careful. Then the three of us sat there, feeling proud and yet a little foolish too, because we weren't children any more.

'What are we supposed to do now?' said Cookie.

'We row the boat to China,' said Colin, using his spade like an oar.

We all three rowed wildly, singing the Row-row-row-your-boat song, waiting for the sea to come splashing up around us.

'I wish we could keep it. It's a magnificent boat,' I said wistfully.

'We can build another boat tomorrow,' said Cookie.

'Yeah, we'll build an even bigger boat tomorrow,' said Colin. 'A houseboat, with a proper room inside, with beds and benches and all sorts.'

'No, no, a cruiser the length of the beach,' said Cookie.

'Like the *Queen Elizabeth*. Only we'll call it the *Queen Jacky*!' said Colin, cackling with laughter.

Cookie came with us back to the hotel. 'I wish I was staying here too,' he said.

'Yeah, I shall have Jacky all to myself every evening *and* every morning before breakfast.' Colin thumped his chest Tarzan-style and gave a loud jungle yodel.

I shook my head at him. 'Idiot!' Then I looked at Cookie. 'See you tomorrow then?'

I saw him every single day. I wanted to stay with them all the time but I was forced to go on all the outings Biddy and Grace had planned, though I always had several hours on the beach with Cookie and Colin. I plucked up the courage to go swimming with them – at least I could retire into the beach hut to change into my costume, rather than struggling inelegantly under a towel.

I blushed as I stepped outside in my blue and white swimming costume. It suddenly seemed much too skimpy and revealing. Colin wolf-whistled, inevitably, but Cookie smiled at me and held out his hand to take me down to the sea. We ran right into the water and started jumping each wave and then diving like otters until our eyes were stinging with the salt.

We queued at the surf shack another day and I showed off my surfboard skills to both boys, and then we went back to the beach hut and wrapped ourselves in big towels and ate sandwiches from the Oxo tin.

Biddy was worried that the Cooksons might think I was sponging off them, so she gave me money to treat everyone to ice creams. Mrs Cookson invited Biddy and Harry and Ron and Grace to the beach hut and the adults all had a cup of tea together while we fidgeted and fussed, and then declared we were going off for a walk.

We splashed along at the sea's edge, Colin and Cookie often wrestling and fooling around or telling idiotic jokes or making stupid noises. I'd get impatient and think, *What am I doing here with these two loonies*? and I'd wish myself back with my books and my journal. Then Cookie would suddenly take my hand or Colin would say something so utterly silly I'd burst out laughing, and I'd realize I wanted to be with them more than anyone else in the world.

Well . . . I liked Colin very much, fool that he was, but I liked Cookie much more. Whenever Colin whooped off by himself for a minute or two we talked hurriedly, suddenly serious. Once or twice Cookie said, 'Let's push off, just you and me, just for a little while, please.'

'But what about Colin? Wouldn't it hurt his

feelings if we push off by ourselves?' I asked anxiously.

'Oh, never mind Colin,' said Cookie – but he was just as concerned about upsetting him as I was. We stayed a threesome all week.

We went exploring in the caves one afternoon. I was initially disappointed. They were damp and chilly and rather smelly. Every now and then you slipped on empty crisp packets or tripped over beer bottles. Still, it was fun feeling our way through all the winding passages. There was always a thrilling clutch of fear that we would get totally lost and end up going further and further into the dark interior. The constant drip of water from the roof made me wonder if the sea could possibly suddenly come surging in . . .

Colin was very taken up by the echo possibilities in the caves and went running ahead, yodelling enthusiastically. I sighed and went to follow him, but Cookie held onto me, steering me round a rocky boulder. He didn't say anything. He just put his arms round me and bent his head and kissed me. I kissed him back, clinging to him, and for a few moments we were lost in our world – but then a manic cry circled round our heads: '*Jackyyyyyyyy – Cookieeeeeeee!*' We laughed and went to find Colin.

I spent far more time with Colin than with

Cookie, because we had our evening meal back at the hotel. I got changed quickly and went down to the recreation room, where Colin and I played endless games of ping-pong, plus a silly version of Snakes and Ladders, going up every snake and down every ladder.

There was a special dance at our hotel on Friday evening.

'So *I'll* be dancing with Jacky all evening,' Colin crowed triumphantly.

'No, *I* will,' said Cookie. 'I'll come to the dance.'

'It's meant to be for residents only,' said Colin.

'And their guests,' said Cookie firmly. He looked me in the eye. 'I'm definitely coming.'

I didn't fool around playing games with Colin on Friday before dinner. I locked myself in the communal bathroom, ignoring the rattles on the door from the other guests. I washed all the salt out of my hair and had a quick bath. Then, back in my room, I changed into my white dress with the apricot sash. I was really brown now so it looked good on me. I didn't bother with much make-up, just mascara and lipstick. I stared at myself in the mirror. It was as if I was looking at a girl in a picture, not *me*. I seemed to have stepped out of myself into a strange new girl who totally startled me. I clutched the edge of the mirror, wanting to hang onto myself in this moment.

I could barely eat my dinner I felt so excited. We all went into the ballroom and sat at little gilt tables around the edges of the room. I sat with Biddy and Harry and Ron and Grace. Ron bought us all a round of drinks and started clowning about. Biddy laughed at his antics, but Harry and Grace stayed po-faced. I think they were both glad we were going home tomorrow. Biddy and Ron were probably sad. And I was desperate. I wanted to stay here in Newquay with Cookie for ever.

I kept peering all round the room for him but he wasn't there. People started plucking up the courage to dance. I did a waltz with Harry, a quickstep with silly twiddly bits with Ron. Colin clearly wasn't up to any kind of ballroom dancing, but he came charging across the room when they announced a jiving session. He couldn't actually jive either, but he jerked around and clicked his fingers and kicked his legs while I circled him, spinning round until I was dizzy.

I leaned against the wall, the room still spinning even though I was still, and saw Cookie walking calmly through the French windows at the end of the room, in a white shirt and black trousers, his hair gleaming gold.

I rubbed my eyes, wondering if I was just imagining him, but he came right up to me, smiling.

'Hello, Jacky. Do you want to dance?' he said.

I danced with him for the rest of the evening. Whenever there was a jiving session Colin joined in too, the three of us gyrating on the spot in our odd trio.

Then I danced a slow foxtrot with Cookie, the two of us shuffling gently about the room. His arms were round my waist, my cheek was touching his, but we couldn't get really close in front of everyone, especially not Biddy and Harry.

'Shall we go outside for a bit?' Cookie whispered into my ear.

I nodded. We simply held hands and walked through the French windows into the hotel garden. It was so cool and quiet there after the noise and clamour of the dance floor. We stood still, breathing in the sweet smells of stocks and roses. But then we heard giggling behind us, and another couple stumbled out into the garden too.

'Let's go for a little walk,' said Cookie. 'Shall we go to the beach?'

'Yes, let's,' I said.

I didn't go back to tell Biddy where I was going. We simply linked fingers and walked out of the garden, down the road, towards the sea. We looked up at the moon and tried counting the stars.

'Do you know what they're all called?' Cookie asked.

'Well, that's the Pole Star,' I said, peering up at the brightest and biggest star. 'And could that be the Great Bear, that cluster there? And I think that's the Pleiades, seven stars together, the smallest in the sky. One of them's called Maia.'

'You've been reading an astronomy book.'

'No, it's *Mary Poppins*. Maia was my favourite character,' I said. 'Did you read it, Cookie?'

'I think my sister did. I read the Jennings books. And William. They didn't tell you about stars. I know all about space though, from Dan Dare in the *Eagle* comic.'

'Well, we're both well-informed then,' I said as we got to the beach.

The sea sucked at the sands, the shushing sound seeming louder at night. I slipped off my heels and stepped onto the beach.

'The sand feels so much colder now,' I said.

'We won't go for a paddle then, we don't want to freeze,' said Cookie. 'You're not too cold now, are you, Jacky?' He put his arm round me. 'Here, I'll warm you up a bit.'

'I'm fine,' I said, snuggling into him. 'This is lovely. I've never been for a moonlit walk before.'

'I like walking in the dark. There's this graveyard near where I live. When I was a little kid it spooked me out and I thought there were all these ghosts hanging round the gravestones. I felt embarrassed I was so scared. I even had nightmares about it, so one day I forced myself to go there by myself. I was actually shaking like a leaf, but when I got in the graveyard it was fine. It was so peaceful, and I just walked around touching all the gravestones, and ever since then I like to cut through the graveyard and have a little quiet time there. Do you think I'm a bit crazy?'

'No, I think you're the most interesting boy I've ever met,' I said truthfully.

'No, I'm not, I can't be – but you're *definitely* the most interesting girl I've ever met,' said Cookie, and he stopped and kissed me.

We didn't quite have the beach to ourselves. There was a dim glow from a barbecue party down at one end, and several mad surfers were yelling in the water.

'Come with me,' said Cookie, and we went into the caves.

It was so dark I couldn't see anything at all. I had to cling to Cookie and he clung to me, and then we were kissing and whispering and wishing we could stay there for ever.

Neither of us had watches. It was very very late when we eventually walked back up the beach towards the hotel.

'So I suppose this is goodbye,' Cookie said.

'Oh, I wish it wasn't,' I said, putting my arms round his neck.

'I've scribbled my address – here,' said Cookie, tucking a piece of paper into my pocket. 'Will you write to me?'

'Of course I will!'

'And we'll maybe meet up again next summer?'

'Yes!'

'And you won't ever forget me?'

'I'll never ever forget you,' I said, and then we kissed goodbye for the last time.

I did write to him, of course, a long long letter, page after page of my innermost thoughts. He wrote back to me, just two sides of paper, but he addressed me as 'Darling Jacky' and signed it 'Love from Cookie'.

I wrote again. I had to wait a week or more before I got an answer, just a postcard this time, with a lot of boring stuff about his school. I wrote a proper letter – and then another – and another. Eventually I got a letter back – *from his mother*! She was very sweet, and said how the whole family had enjoyed meeting me and that Cookie was very fond of me – 'but I'm afraid he's not very good at writing letters'.

I wrote back to thank her. And that was it. I never heard from Cookie again, and we didn't go back to Cornwall the following summer. I was heartbroken. So what did I do? I wrote about it.

The next year I started a new, more elaborate journal. I wrote in it in February 1961:

Ever since last Summer I've been trying to write a novel. This was vaguely based on last summer holiday, and dealt with Cookie in detail. I was convinced that I was writing what was to become a great classic, and dabbled around with it at the weekends and in the evenings. I now know that it was only very adolescent escapism. I had no boyfriend or anything, and in the Summer I had spent a nice week with Cookie, so I unconsciously comforted myself by my very infantile book about my 'adult' experience.

I was pretty hard on myself! I wish I still had that story now. Later, in April, writing in my diary I said:

Hello. I've nothing much to write about as today was so quiet and ordinary, so I'll write down anything that comes into my head. The nice thing about keeping this diary is that I write about everything without being laughed at; I can write down secrets with no fear of them being told; I can just scribble away to my heart's content. I don't even have to worry about writing or spelling because I don't mind a bit if I'm untidy. You get a lovely sense of freedom this way. It's funny, I'm getting very enthusiastic about diary writing, and yet when I was on holiday I decided to give it up. I'm still terribly conceited – I thought I would write a full length novel based on my Bruges holiday [a school trip that Easter, my first time abroad]. *All this time and I'm still not cured. After several attempts to begin I wisely admitted defeat and returned to you. But I'm still not crushed – I'm going to write a book, but not yet, because 15 is too young, too immature. After all, I wanted to write a book at 14, about last summer. I thought I knew it all; now my attitude has changed completely and I feel much more grown up, and yet not so superior. I know I'm just a silly little fool, probably with absolutely no gift for writing at all, yet that doesn't prevent me from trying. I've got to be a writer and nothing else.*

I kept further diaries throughout my teenage years (though I had to hide them from Biddy!).

Best keep it under the matress.

She certainly didn't approve of my boyfriends!

I left home at 17 and worked as a journalist in Dundee.

My first short story in print!

I had my first novel published when I was 23.

I can't believe it! My book on display!

HIDE AND SEEK

JACQUELINE WILSON

NEW TITLES

I told my daughter Emma lots of stories.

Tell me a story, Mum!

There was once a little girl called Emma . . .

Then I had an idea for a story about a fierce little girl in a children's home

The Story of Tracy Beaker!

I met Nick Sharratt and he's illustrated my books ever since.

That's so great, Nick! She looks exactly how I imagined her.

Nick and I have worked together on over forty books so far. Let's hope there are LOTS more. I've lost count of the number of imaginary children I've invented. See how many you can recognize . . .

TO BE CONTINUED...

Join the FREE online

Jacqueline Wilson

 ⭐ FAN CLUB ⭐

Read Jacqueline's monthly diary, look up
tour info, receive fan club e-newsletters.

All this and more, including a fab
message board, members'
jokes and loads of exclusive top offers

Visit **www.jacquelinewilson.co.uk**
for more info!

JACQUELINE WILSON was born in Bath in 1945, but has spent most of her life in Kingston-upon-Thames, Surrey. She always wanted to be a writer and wrote her first 'novel' when she was nine, filling countless Woolworths' exercise books as she grew up. She started work at a publishing company and then went on to work as a journalist on *Jackie* magazine (which was named after her) before turning to writing fiction full-time.

Since 1990 Jacqueline has written prolifically for children and has won many of the top awards for children's books, including the *Guardian* Children's Fiction Award, the Smarties Prize, the Red House Book Award and the Children's Book of the Year. Jacqueline was awarded an OBE in the Queen's Birthday Honours list in 2002 and was made a Dame in 2008. She was the Children's Laureate in 2005–2007. She is the most borrowed author of all from British libraries and an astounding twenty-five million copies of her books have now been sold in the UK.

An avid reader herself, Jacqueline has a personal collection of many, many thousands of books. She has one grown-up daughter.

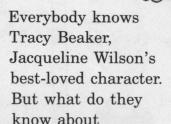

Everybody knows Tracy Beaker, Jacqueline Wilson's best-loved character. But what do they know about Jacqueline herself?

In this fascinating book, discover . . .

. . . how Jacky dealt with an unpredictable father,
like Prue in *Love Lessons*.
. . . how she chose new toys in Hamleys,
like Dolphin in *The Illustrated Mum*.
. . . how she sat entrance exams,
like Ruby in *Double Act*.

But most of all discover how Jacky loved reading and
writing stories. From the very first story she wrote, it
was clear that this little girl had a vivid imagination.
But who would've guessed that she would grow up
to be a bestselling, award-winning author!

Includes previously unseen photos, Jacqueline's
own school reports and a brand new chapter from
Jacqueline on the response to the book, her
teenage years and more!